Gen 2:7
Believe and do u
believe. Do
... become reckless
unreasonable, unjust, Tyrannical,
criminal, boldly stupid,
unmitigated depravity
.. abandon, honesty, decency, morality
minds disconnected from good ...

MADE IN HIS IMAGE

Examining the Complexities of the Human Body

Self-righteousness married to total
relativism is a terrifying thing.
~~Theory of Intelligent Intervention~~ by
Invention.

Randy J. Guliuzza

Uncertainty, doubt, fear, guilt.
Anger,
Crafted ...

ICR
INSTITUTE FOR
CREATION
RESEARCH

What are you your life for?
What is your life's purpose?
What is your vision? What is
your dream for the future?

Atheists are conflicted in that
they have a tremendous reliance
on random chance while claiming
to be rational.
Do you waste ~~spend~~ a lot of time and
money in casinos hoping for
"Lady luck" to ~~like~~ favor you?

MADE IN HIS IMAGE
Examining the Complexities of the Human Body
BY RANDY J. GULIUZZA, P.E., M.D.

First printing: November 2009

All Scripture quotations are from the New King James Version.

ISBN: 978-0-932766-99-1
Library of Congress Catalog Number: 2009940303

Please visit our website for other books and resources: ICR.org

Printed in the United States of America.

Humans are not simple.
Life is NOT simple!
Luck or logic
Random or planned

Checks and balances within a system and among systems.

Table of Contents

The magic of error messages/coding
mutated

The complexity of human

Exchange of information, signals, codes within
the body at the conscious & unconscious levels

Nothing simple
Nothing random - it fits out of
forethought (Intelligence),
design and engineering.

Organisms are designed to
cope with a certain level
of crisis. Anxieties
Flexibility build-in

Life does not begin by throwing
a bunch of chemicals (lucky
coincidence) together.
Fitting properly and purposefully
are of priority also.

Introduction

I rreducible complexity could be summarized as an observed "all-or-nothing unity." An instructional objective of this book is to clearly demonstrate that all systems in people possess this unifying complexity. Creation scientists have been writing about this for decades, particularly at the molecular level. It is unfortunate that the molecular level has become the primary focus of this attribute since this complexity is found even lower, at the information level, and also higher, at the organ, system, and organism levels. In fact, it extends to the ecosystem level since the body uses all its systems—fully integrated together—to ingeniously exploit things in nature like inertia, momentum, gravity, properties of gases, sunlight, and so forth. This powerful design argument has been addressed by evolutionists, but not defeated.

The information for this book was obtained primarily from published technical literature and from current editions of the most popular anatomy and physiology textbooks. Because much of this information is basic medical data and can be readily found and verified, in both the articles and answer sections, footnotes have been omitted.

"Complexity" is the key word in the title of this book,

because it stands in such contrast to a favorite word in evolutionary literature: *simple.* To show that there is nothing simple in biological systems, this book was written from the unique perspective of a professional engineer who is also a physician. Having worked in both the engineering and medical professions for several decades, it is evident that most in these two professions have a wholly different appreciation of complex systems.

Biological professionals study things that are *already built.* The writings of many—particularly evolutionary biologists—indicate that they do not even see engineering interactions right in front of them. To the untrained eye, things always look much simpler, and changes appear easier to execute, than they really are. Though some may appreciate certain levels of complexity, since most have never designed or built anything from scratch, they put a very high—yet unjustifiable—faith in the constructive powers of chance, luck, and genetic tinkering or tweaking. Like amateur artists looking at paintings of the great masters, so many important details are totally missed and they do not appreciate levels of complexity in the same way another master artist would.

Many times engineers are tasked with bringing a *totally new* item into existence. Not just anything or something, but projects that ultimately have an intended purpose. Engineers recognize the difficulty of coming up with ideas from scratch on how to do it…and achieve a balance on satisfying all needs—even ones that are opposed to each other. They know that the best solutions are mini-flashes of genius—called ingenious ideas—that elicit a "Wow, who would have ever thought of that?" response. The next hurdle is to find or make devices (motors, transmissions, etc.) to execute the ideas. It seems that only engineers fully appreciate the

6

hardest step of all, which is controlling those devices by knowing
what is happening at any moment and integrating methods to
make rapid adjustments. Testing, problem solving (debugging),
writing detailed plans and specifications in order to build and
operate everything, are all important follow-on steps.

All of these can be herculean tasks, and to get the fullest professional respect from other engineers, everything in the process
must be safe, readily buildable, achieve maximum results with
minimum resources, and withstand a reasonable amount of
abuse without breaking. Systems of the human body show *all* of
these features—at levels that should evoke the greatest respect,
indeed adoration, from every engineer for the finest Engineer of
all, the Lord Jesus Christ.

It is a goal of this book to highlight these design features
so anyone can see them, and thus be certain of the Bible's state-
ments that from the beginning, people were fully functional, fully
human, and fully created in His image.

Human body systems:
Interfaced, not a hold over from
another kind of organism.
A Remodeling mess!

Balancing with movement _ complex
Maintaing
Difficult _ extremely complicated _
All these numerous parts working together.
Sensors giving feedback. Adjustments
Fine Tuning. Control systems.

* what are the purpose(s) of your eyes?
What components must fit together
   for these purposes?

What is the scientific proof that evolution by
common descent from microbe to
man occurred by good luck?

Naturalistic _ "Luck" is god like
           "Time" "   "   "
   Errors in copying _ "   "

phenomenal ability, sense, sensors
inertia, momentum, force, accelerate
Unity: Naturalist impose too much burden,
credit to luck.
Babies fall, learn to crawl, then walk.
Walking upright on 2 legs.
Complexity of movements

I

Beauty in Motion

How is it possible - Sensors detect

why do

Humans possess a phenomenal ability to roll, twist, spin, jump, twirl, flip, run, leap, and lunge, as a single motion or in complex combinations, in bare feet or with slippers, shoes, skates, skis, boards or rollers, forward or backward, on one leg or with two, or simply to balance motionless on one arm or tiptoe on the top of a champagne bottle. Ballerinas, gymnasts, and ice skaters depend on their bodies' ability to not only balance, but also to sense speed of rotation and body position, and then make just the right body adjustments. How does all of this work together?

Just like man-made control systems, the first step to controlling a body is to sense what is happening to it. Two important sensors detect *inertia* and *momentum*. Inertia is the property of objects to resist being moved. It takes a certain amount of force to move an object from a dead stop, or to make it move faster or slower. More force is needed to accelerate a rock than a feather. When an object is already moving, momentum is the property that operates to keep it moving. A moving rock has

Complex Sensors Unique to human

Def

9

Which was the precursor organism and which ability evolved that was not in the precursor organism?

maculae, electrochemical impulses
otoliths, limestone, gravitational pull,
interdependent components

more momentum than a feather at the same speed.

Sensing Straight-Line Movements

Maculae

Sensors in the inner ear detect inertia and momentum linked with straight-line accelerations. These *maculae* have many parts, but three interdependent components, stacked like a sandwich, are key. Attached to the skull is the base component—a patch of support cells surrounding rows of specialized "hair cells," which generate electrochemical impulses. The hair cell has four very short hair-like projections on top that regulate how fast the signals are sent according to which direction the hairs are bent.

The middle layer is a gelatin-like substance. The hairs from below stick up and are embedded in the gelatin. The top layer is, amazingly, a mat of hundreds of tiny rock crystals or *otoliths* (literally "ear stones") made of the same material as limestone. It is like having a plate containing a block of gelatin with a heavier plate on top. A quick push on the bottom plate causes the gelatin to flex until the top plate matches the same speed as the bottom plate.

In maculae, head movements cause the rock layer on the gelatin to "jiggle" in relation to the base. The distance it moves is smaller than a hair's width, but that tiny motion is still detected. Using heavy rock material for the top is a brilliant choice, since it ensures that even slight accelerations generate a force strong enough to be identified. Remarkably, these components are bundled in a package about the size of a grain of rice. The body has two sensors—suitably oriented with one perpendicular and one parallel to the earth's gravitational pull—located on each side of the head.

Maculae

Components ↓
1) "hair cells" – attached to skull
2) gelatin
Top layer 3) rock crystals

10

So how do they work? With forward movement, inertia momentarily holds the rock layer still and the gelatin allows the base to slide forward in relation to the rock layer, for a time as short as *1/1000 of a second,* until the rock layer catches up. The gelatin and hair cell projections flex backward, sending faster signals to the brain. When movement stops, the rock layer's *momentum* carries it forward, the hair projections are bent forward, decreasing the signals sent. The other sensor works similarly when the body is moved up and down in an elevator. This design alerts a person only when changes to speed happen and does not constantly annoy a person with alerts when speed is steady—which is the exact information people need.

Sensing Rotary Movement

Rotating movements on an axis (rolls, spins, or cartwheels) are detected by another inner ear sensor called *semicircular canals.* This sensor uses three tiny round tubes formed directly in the skull—the optimal shape for detecting rotary motion. Their orientation allows rotations in any possible axis to be detected. An inner membrane covering produces a fluid called *endolymph,* which completely fills the inside. Since it is a fluid, it will slip relative to the bony tube when rotation starts, but quickly attains the same speed if rotation continues.

Motion detectors protrude into the endolymph. They are composed of hair cells with hair-like projections embedded in a mobile gelatin-like mass called a *cupula.* When a body spins one direction, inertia momentarily holds the endolymph still, which deflects the cupula in the opposite direction until the endolymph catches up. Bending the hair cell projections one way

11

sends faster signals to the brain. When the spin stops, the endo-lymph's momentum carries it past the now stopped cupula, and the cupula deflects the opposite way, decreasing the signals sent. Extremely sensitive, each round tube can detect rotary accelerations as low as 0.1 degree/second^2.

Sensing Head and Other Muscle Movement

This description of these receptors is very simplistic, but they are actually complex mechanical-electrical devices with housings formed right into a baby's skull as it develops in the womb. But even these are not enough. Visual input—not just what the eyes see but also where they are aimed—is sensed and that huge volume of data is sent to the brain.

Thousands of sensors in skeletal muscles monitoring the sum of internal forces and rates of contraction also send data. Sensors in tendons send data on even the slightest changes in tension between muscle and bone. Even internal pressures of fluids in capsules surrounding major joints like the knee joint are checked. To give an idea of the enormous quantity of data reaching the brain, the signal rate from just the maculae monitoring only linear motion while at rest is about two million impulses per second. Now add signals from all of the thousands of other sensors and include the signal rate changes due to motion!

The Brain Integrates Sensations with Body Movement

The part of the brain managing much of this data and turning it into information is the cerebellum. It contributes only 10 percent of brain mass but contains nearly 50 percent of the

*neurons, Comparisons, memory patterns
learned, innate, mathematical equations
fine-tune, feedback, corrections
robotics, "isolated system" = No! All systems
on*

neurons in the brain. Why? Because the data it manipulates in just one second would either fry the world's best supercomputer at the same speed or take years to process at normal speeds.

Think of a gymnast learning a vault. Huge arrays of information are compared, analyzed, and adjusted at blindingly fast speeds. Data from all sensors as well as data from the eyes are continuously compared to each other. This voluminous data array is compared to memory patterns, learned and innate, stored in the brain to correctly identify the actions happening to the body. This comparison is equivalent to solving hundreds of complex mathematical equations.

The information is then compared to another vast array sent from the motion planning part of the brain in order to fine-tune plans for dozens of muscle movements simultaneously. Then as the body executes the motion, feedback from motion and muscle sensors is rapidly and constantly compared to the plan and any deviations are corrected until the vault ends. Contrast that to robot designers who celebrate for just getting a robot to walk on level ground—now let it respond to a stiff gust of wind.

Conclusion

It is clear that there is no such thing as an isolated "balance system." The body uses all of its systems to balance and, in the process, ingeniously exploits properties of nature such as inertia, momentum, and gravity. In this area, humans are unmatched. No human-engineered device can come close. Even strong and nimble animals can't compare. The ability for humans to spin, flip, etc., may confer some supposed survival value. However,

better explanation, attributes

when considering the graceful yet powerful performance of an ice skater or gymnast, a better explanation is that humans share a certain attribute with their Creator, the Lord Jesus Christ—an appreciation for beauty.

Who can begin to grasp the knowledge and capability of the Lord Jesus? What He creates integrates so many properties of nature it leaves no doubt that He is Lord of all.

Integrated systems.
Coordinated actions

Beauty in Motion
Devotional Thought

Yet I will rejoice in the LORD, I will joy in the God of my salvation. The LORD God is my strength; He will make my feet like deer's feet, and He will make me walk on my high hills. (Habakkuk 3:18-19)

Both Habakkuk and David (Psalm 18:33-34) compared their feet to those of the deer when they are walking in the strength of the Lord. David made his comparison in the context of the Lord's help when he had to go forth to war and how he had swiftness, a sure footing, and other skills beneficial in battle, so the comparison is probably not purely figurative. With highest respect to the abilities of the deer, humans actually possess some physical capabilities in terms of ability to spin, roll, twist, or balance that exceed that of any animal. This ability should not be surprising since the Lord made man in His image and even the physical or athletic prowess of humans should express His glory—in addition to the mental and spiritual dimensions of people. That is yet another gift for which we also can rejoice in the Lord.

Maculae: what it is, what it does.
How did it come to be?

Questions

1. The *maculae* in the inner ear are able to detect properties of objects, one that resists being moved (inertia), and the one that wants to keep them moving (momentum). Why does it take a huge amount of faith in the power of "luck" to give an evolutionary explanation for the existence of maculae? In order to get a functioning sensor, what are some of the parts that would need to be in place?

Luck
or
Design?

2. A vital part of the maculae is a patch of specialized cells called *hair cells*, which can generate electrochemical impulses and regulate how fast the signals are sent depending on which direction they are bent. Research some physiology textbooks or scientific papers on the Internet. What is the standard evolutionary explanation for the origination of these cells? Is this type of explanation common for any other types of structures?

Hair cells as the part of the maculae.
How did they originate?

3. Picture a gymnast completing a vault. Name some of the things that her body must <u>monitor</u> in order for her to complete the maneuver correctly.

Mutation - accidently get it to work right
Simple structures coupled
Data - sense, transmit, interpret, respond

Answers

1. The maculae exploit physical properties of nature. There is a big problem with using a property of nature because until there is some way to sense it, there is no way to know that it is even there! According to naturalistic evolution, there is no supernatural designing force that would have had knowledge of inertia and momentum to preplan the development of any structures. Since these two phenomena are essentially laws of motion, evolutionists must believe that somehow, somewhere in the past a mutation led to the accidental formation of some type of "simple" structure that was able to be moved, which eventually became coupled to a neurological sensor that could send a varying amount of signal, which became coupled to a nervous system of which one portion eventually developed the ability to accept the data and interpret it as information. The whole process posited by evolutionists absolutely depends on some organism being "lucky" enough to get some type of rudimentary sensor to the properties of motion at some time early in the development of life. Of course, from actual observations in nature, there is no such thing as a rudimentary sensor. They are all complex—even ones evolutionists call "simple."

2. The standard evolutionary explanation for the origination of these hair cells, as well as other sensors for motion, temperature, pain, etc., is that they are simply "modified" neurons. No further explanation is provided of how they became modified or what function they served until they were fully modified. The milk ducts in the female breast are also claimed to be simply modified sweat glands. No explanation is given for how long infants nursed on sweat until fully functional milk

female breast - simply mod. fuil sweat glands(?)

ducts evolved. Sometimes the simply "modified" explanation
is cloaked in jargon with words like "co-opted"—e.g., parts of
a flagellum were "co-opted" from parts of a type of secretory
system and then these parts were eventually "modified."

3. From the start, the gymnast must monitor the following: running speed, timing of jump, force of the jump, forward rotation and timing for her hands to land on the vault horse, pressure to push off the horse, speed of any rotations and tucks,
timing of body position for landing, and the pressure in all of
her body muscles (especially lower legs) for the landing. Now
that the goal of performance is in mind, consider how challenging a task this will be to design a robot able to complete a
vault with a single twist followed by a forward rotation.

1) May seem like a S
   What is the purpose of your _____ cars ?
   (s)

2) What components of your eyes must fit together
   ↑ in order for you to _____ hear ?

plays a had (5-11-18)

3) Which of the _____ + _____ ,
   which evolved first ? _____

4) How many mutated genes were
   involved in the change from
   non human e. _____ to human _____ ?

19

A tall tale - A fairy tale !

Notes

_____

_____

_____

_____

_____

_____

_____

_____

_____

_____

_____

_____

_____

_____

_____

_____

_____

_____

_____

_____

Notes

_____

_____

_____

_____

_____

_____

_____

_____

_____

_____

_____

_____

_____

_____

_____

_____

_____

_____

_____

_____

2
Breath of Life

I n American football, the quarterback can hand off the
football to a team member, who then may do a handoff
to another player. Exciting plays may be put together that
combine several handoffs and even a pass downfield to an
awaiting player who, hopefully, carries the ball to the goal.

The handoff is a great idea that was used long before football came along. In fact, it is a key factor in the human respiratory system. There, the "goal" is to take molecules of oxygen
gas (O_2), "hand them off" to all body tissues, and then transfer
carbon dioxide gas (CO_2) out of those tissues back to the atmosphere. Intelligent players move a football, but the human body
accomplishes its handoffs with unthinking molecules that use
the laws of nature and the same physical components to move
the gases both ways.

Natural Handoffs

Recall that breathable air is about 78 percent nitrogen, 21
percent O_2, and the remaining gases—including CO_2—are less

than 1 percent. The combined weight, or force, of these gases pushing on a surface is called its *pressure*. Oxygen itself contributes a "partial" pressure of 21 percent of the total. In the human body, the amount of O_2 is highest in the lungs, so the pressure of O_2 in lungs is greater than in muscle. (Muscle tissue is used here to represent all tissues in a person's body.)

Why is this important? Because the human respiratory system utilizes a principle of nature that gas *exchanges* go from places of high pressure to low pressure—that's one way a handoff is done.

The respiratory system also exploits two other natural phenomena. Some gases will dissolve in liquids, just like CO_2 does in a can of soda. Gases may dissolve easier in certain liquids. How easily a gas dissolves in a liquid is called its *solubility*. Moving liquids transport the dissolved gas, but under the right conditions they let the gas escape—which is another type of handoff.

Finally, some tissue molecules "like" to grab and hold gases. How strongly they bind them is called the molecule's *affinity* for that gas. When one low affinity tissue turns over a gas to a high affinity tissue, a third type of handoff happens.

Partial Pressures

The normal conditions in the atmosphere *compared* to those inside the body are such that the pressure of O_2 in the air is higher than in lungs, which is higher than in blood, which is higher than in muscles. Oxygen is handed off on each step from areas of high to low pressure. Muscles "burn" sugar molecules for energy best using O_2, which results in CO_2 as waste. Carbon dioxide gets pushed out of the body from high to low pressure, since CO_2 pressure in muscles is higher than in blood, which is higher than in lungs, which is higher than in a normal atmosphere.

Based on Earth's concentrations of atmospheric gases, it just "happens" that the body's concentration of O_2 as a combustion source and CO_2 as a waste product are able to take advantage of the principle of *partial pressures*. However, at every step the *speed* of exchange is vital, and key molecules made in the body enable the handoffs to go extremely fast—fast enough to support life.

Hemoglobin Carries Oxygen

The components of blood are essential for life. Blood is made up mostly of a liquid called *plasma*, which carries red blood cells. Plasma is mainly water, but O_2 is poorly soluble in water. If humans relied on dissolved O_2 in the water portion *alone* to supply the body, a person's resting heart rate would need to be 1,050 beats (contractions) per minute even if it could pump the same volume of blood with each beat as under normal conditions (which it cannot).

The problem is solved with a molecule packaged within red cells called *hemoglobin*, which rapidly binds and transports 99 percent of all O_2. Hemoglobin consists of four protein-*heme* subunits. Heme holds an iron atom that helps bind O_2 and thereby turns bright red. Thus, one hemoglobin carries four O_2 molecules.

Hemoglobin's performance is optimized not only by its components, but also by its shape. Surprisingly, once the first O_2 molecule is bound, hemoglobin continuously changes shape so the rate of loading for each remaining O_2 molecule is a *faster* rate than the one before it. At rest, every minute the heart will pump over one gallon of oxygen-saturated hemoglobin via red cells to active tissues that are constantly in need of a fresh supply.

Oxygen Offloads to Muscle

Oxygen-holding proteins in muscle are called *myoglobin.* Myoglobin wants O_2 and, in fact, its shape lends naturally to an even higher affinity for O_2 than hemoglobin. So O_2 moves from blood to muscle just as it's needed.

But the environment in muscle tissue actually accelerates the offloading of O_2. How? First, high CO_2 concentrations actually force a faster *release* of O_2. The attraction for O_2 is high due to a very low partial pressure of O_2. Then once again, unloading the first O_2 molecule induces hemoglobin to change shape, so the rate of O_2 unloading gets progressively faster.

Removing Carbon Dioxide

Transport of CO_2 back to the lungs fulfills two life-sustaining functions: offloading a deadly waste product, and helping to keep the internal acid-base conditions in perfect balance so other biochemical processes can happen. Water will combine with CO_2 in red cells to form carbonic acid, which is almost immediately pushed into plasma as a (+) hydrogen ion and a (-) bicarbonate ion. These form a huge pool of ions that can be finely tuned to keep body pH in a tight range.

However, water and CO_2 naturally combine too slowly under normal conditions, thus requiring days of reaction time. That problem is solved by an enzyme in red cells called *carbonic anhydrase* that completes the reaction—going both ways—in a fraction of a second.

Alveoli Gas Exchanges

Every minute, 25 billion red cells move through lung tissues, so gas exchange speeds are again crucial. Each cell can spend only 0.75 second in units called *alveoli* where exchanges take place.

Engineers that design structures to exchange heat or gases know that the central factors are the total surface area and the properties of the medium. If the surface area for all alveoli in lungs was flattened out, it would cover the floor of about a 960-square-foot house with a membrane that has about the thickness of a human hair. (For an average adult, this is 40 times the total surface area of his skin.)

The natural pressure difference from atmosphere to lung is high for O_2 but lower for CO_2, resulting in different exchange rates—but an equal quantity of these gases *must* be swapped. It just "happens" that the solubility of CO_2 in plasma *and* alveolar fluids is 20 times higher than O_2, which is just right to compensate for the pressure differences. So, equal amounts of these gases are exchanged in less than 0.25 second—leaving over 0.5 second to spare.

Fetal Hemoglobin

Astute readers may protest, "I can see how the gas exchanges from blood to tissue because of the different conditions involved. But a baby forming in the womb uses the placenta to exchange gases from the mother's *blood* to the baby's *blood*. Mom and baby's red cells will bind O_2 and CO_2 *equally* well. Blood-to-blood exchanges will fail and the baby will die from lack of O_2."

Not if the baby in the womb has a *different kind* of blood from his mother! Amazingly, the baby's *fetal* hemoglobin has a higher affinity for O_2 (and several other things) than mom's. So gases do exchange properly. Once born, genetic switches for hemoglobin production within bone marrow will automatically "turn off" for fetal and "turn on" for the adult kind—which is better suited for life outside the womb. The transition is finished in about four months.

Conclusion

Who would have thought that a few principles of nature like solubility and partial pressures would be so important for life? The Lord Jesus Christ did! He crafted the essential enzymes, hemoglobin, membranes, blood vessels, muscles, and dozens of other tissues necessary to utilize those principles. *All things* definitely work after the counsel of His own will, just as the Bible says (Ephesians 1:11).

Pride, self-exultation

Breath of Life
Devotional Thought

For as I was passing through and considering the objects of your worship, I even found an altar with this inscription: TO THE UNKNOWN GOD. Therefore, the One whom you worship without knowing, Him I proclaim to you: "God, who made the world and everything in it, since He is Lord of heaven and earth, does not dwell in temples made with hands. Nor is He worshiped with men's hands, as though He needed anything, since He gives to all life, breath, and all things. (Acts 17:23-25)

Paul was speaking on Mars Hill in Athens, Greece, to the intellectual crowd and strongly reminded them that God is the Maker of all things and that He is not beholden to them for anything, such as a temple in which to dwell, but that they were dependent on Him for even their very breath. Now that so much more is known of the intricacies of the human respiratory system—its use of natural phenomena and its many vital specialized compounds—it would seem that most scientists and intellectuals would be the leaders in thanking the Lord Jesus for His great gift of life and breath. But the same self-centered, man-exulting pride found in Athens long ago still blinds the minds of many scientists today from seeing the obvious elements of His designs in nature. It is not that scientific evidence forces them not to see God, but prideful self-exultation prevents them from seeing (or rationalizing away) the overwhelming scientific evidence. However, for those who know Christ, it is a privilege to join with all nature to honor Him: "Let everything that has breath praise the LORD. Praise the LORD!" (Psalm 150:6).

29

Questions

1. The respiratory system will utilize three natural phenomena to exchange gases, partial pressures, solubility, and affinity. In your own words, define what these phenomena are. Compare oxygen to carbon dioxide in relation to these phenomena and the two important molecules that were discussed demonstrating affinity.

2. Important compounds are mentioned that are essential for the respiratory system to function properly. List three. Would the respiratory system—as science knows it—have been able to function without all of these being available right from the beginning?

3. The lungs have the capability to oxygenate a lot of blood in a very short amount of time. They function very much like man-made gas heat exchangers. What are two of these design features? In a physiology textbook or by searching the Internet, look for information on another compound found in lungs called *surfactant* and another found in hemoglobin called 2,3-BPG (or 2,3-DPG). Do these compounds also show any features of design? What is the standard evolutionary explanation for the origination of these things?

Answers

1. The combined weight of atmospheric gases pushing on a surface is called its *pressure*. Each gas itself contributes a "part" of that pressure so each has its own unique "partial" pressure. The partial pressure of oxygen is over 20 times higher than carbon dioxide. The partial pressure of oxygen is higher outside the body, so it tends to push oxygen in; and the partial pressure of carbon dioxide inside the body is greater than atmosphere that tends to push carbon dioxide out. This is what is needed. Some gases will dissolve in liquids just like CO_2 does in a can of soda. Gases may dissolve more easily in certain liquids, and how easily a gas dissolves in a liquid is called its *solubility*. CO_2 is more soluble in plasma (water) than is oxygen. Some tissue molecules "like" to grab and hold gases. How strongly they bind them is called the molecule's *affinity* for that gas. When all the right compounds are in place, myoglobin has a higher affinity for oxygen and lower affinity for carbon dioxide than hemoglobin, so the right gases are exchanged in the correct directions (i.e. hemoglobin carries oxygen to myoglobin and exchanges it for carbon dioxide, which hemoglobin/plasma carries away).

2. Hemoglobin is necessary to transport oxygen since an adequate amount of oxygen cannot be dissolved in plasma alone to meet the body's needs. Carbonic anhydrase allows the water in plasma to combine with CO_2 in red cells to form carbonic acid and then be carried in the plasma as a (+) hydrogen ion and a (-) bicarbonate ion at speeds fast enough to support life. Fetal hemoglobin has a higher affinity for oxygen than adult hemoglobin, so vital gas exchanges go in the right direction;

otherwise the baby would not survive due to oxygen deprivation. For the system to work as is currently known, all of these molecules must have been present from the start of the system.

3. The membrane lining the alveoli is both very thin and permeable enough to allow gases to pass through it. The surface area of this membrane is also very large, which allows for rapid gas exchanges—so large that people can still live with only one lung if the other one needs to be removed. The alveoli in lungs blow up like balloons upon inspiration and collapse on expiration. Remember how hard it is to start to blow up a fully collapsed balloon but easier as the balloon gets bigger? It is even harder for alveoli since they are moist with water and the surface tension of the water molecules tends to stick the insides together and force them to collapse fully. Surfactant is a vital wetting agent that breaks the bond of the water tension and actually allows the alveoli to inflate very easily at the beginning of inspiration and not allow them to collapse fully upon expiration. Without surfactant, people would not be able to inflate their lungs unless they generated tremendous inspiration pressures—most people cannot. The hemoglobin 2,3-BPG binds preferentially to low oxygenated hemoglobin, which stabilizes the low oxygen affinity conformation (shape), making it harder for oxygen to bind hemoglobin and easier for it to be released to adjacent tissues. When tissues are not getting enough oxygen, a "signal" is sent for red blood cells to generate more 2,3-BPG so more oxygen will be released in tissues deprived of oxygen (such as at high altitudes, and diseases causing airway obstructions or congestive heart failure). Evolutionists continue to explain the origination of all of these compounds by

mutations that occurred in the DNA of animals very long ago and these mutations were "conserved"—that is, passed on to their descendants. (DNA found in an animal believed to be ancestral to another animal, in which the DNA is not found, is because, of course, it was "not conserved.")

Notes

_____

_____

_____

_____

_____

_____

_____

_____

_____

_____

_____

_____

_____

_____

_____

_____

_____

_____

_____

_____

_____

3
Balancing Body Temperature

control over body temperature regulation
Core body temperature range 96° – 101°F
Set point = 98.6°F   ± 10° = lethal
area

A major achievement for design engineers is building precise control mechanisms for active processes. Lives depend on the precision in which certain processes are maintained, such as the manufacture of drugs.

Even more vital to survival is the human body's complex, integrated system that maintains precise control over the body's temperature even when it generates tremendous quantities of internal heat through strenuous activity or is exposed to wide-ranging external temperatures.

Temperature Regulation Is Essential for Life

The organs in the skull, chest, and abdomen are the most temperature-sensitive organs in the human body. Biochemical processes, particularly enzyme activities, within these organs are essential for life and function best in a narrow temperature range of 96 to 101°F, which is called the *core* body temperature range. For most people, average temperature is 98.6°F, which is the "set point" established by the master temperature regulator within the brain—the hypothalamus.

If core body temperature varies by about 10°F above or below this range, it poses a high risk of being lethal. Why? For every 1.8°F increase in the core, crucial chemical reaction rates in organs are deranged and increase by 10 percent. Also, as temperatures rise outside the normal range, proteins—particularly enzymes—start losing both their shape and function, while nerve tissue activity is increasingly depressed. Small children risk going into seizures at about 106°F and most people will be dead if the core reaches 109°F. Conversely, if the core is chilled to below 87°F, electrochemical activity in the heart starts becoming so disrupted that most people will die of cardiac arrest.

It is critical to balance the body temperature within the core range. However, the difficulty of that task cannot be fully appreciated without considering the quantity of heat energy the body needs to manage. How much heat does a person generate? Even while sleeping, with skeletal muscles totally relaxed, heat is still produced as a byproduct of basic metabolism. In fact, about 60 percent of daily energy needs—enough heat to raise the temperature of 20 pounds of water about 2°F every hour— is expended just staying alive.

Now add on activities. For every one hour of hard work or exercise, the heat generated could raise the temperature of the same water almost 20°F—and well-trained athletes can produce almost twice as much heat. An increased level of heat production lasts several hours even after activity ceases. Some engineers assert that offices built to optimal energy efficiency could be heated through the winter using only the body heat of the occupants themselves. Depending on the external environment surrounding a person, this generated heat can be a friend or foe—but it must be precisely regulated.

An Integrated Temperature Regulatory Center

The whole brain helps regulate body temperature, but the main thermoregulatory center is the hypothalamus (located midline in the brain behind the eyes), which possesses two specialized sections: a heat-losing center and a heat-promoting center. Just like in man-made systems designed to modulate temperature, a means of sensing the actual temperatures must be in place. The body has two distinct specialized cells—heat sensors and cold sensors called *thermoreceptors*—that are capable of detecting a temperature change as low as 0.4°F. To keep surveillance on the outside world, hundreds of thermoreceptors are optimally located in the skin, mucous membranes of the nose and mouth, the eyes, and in some muscles.

Sensors send impulses to the brain depending on both how fast and how much the temperature changes—as many as 240 impulses per second for each receptor. Data from these sensors is kept organized by being segregated from other input sent to the brain via exclusive pathways in the nervous system.

The data is continuously analyzed by the hypothalamus and converted to information that is compared to a pre-set bank of information that was present from birth. This allows the hypothalamus to anticipate external temperature changes that may affect core temperature and begin processes to adjust body temperature accordingly. The actual core temperature is monitored by the hypothalamus itself using thermoreceptors that measure the temperature of blood within this core organ.

Eliminating Excess Heat

The heat-losing center and heat-promoting center each have body systems under its control that can be regulated to keep heat production equal to heat loss. When one center is stimulated, a concurrent inhibitory signal is sent to the other. So when it is hot outside or increased physical exertion raises the body temperature above the set point, the activated heat-losing center first inhibits the signal to tiny muscle fibers lining blood vessels in the skin. This decreases muscle tone, allowing the vessels to dilate and become flush with warm blood shunted away from the core. The skin acts as a giant radiator that offloads body heat to air currents that carry it away, directly transfers it to cooler objects, or radiates it away as electromagnetic energy.

Using body heat to convert liquid water to a vapor is used continuously to maintain the core. The lungs and the skin each exchange almost a half a quart of water per day to cool the body just for basic needs. When a large heat transfer is needed, sweat glands on the skin can be massively recruited to cover the skin in very tiny droplets that can be easily evaporated. This method works best, because evaporating water removes up to ten times more heat than water that simply runs off in large drops from the skin. When heat-stressed, a person could potentially evaporate off up to two quarts of sweat per hour from the skin.

Maintaining Necessary Heat

When cold conditions threaten to lower the core temperature, the heat-promoting center initiates actions to conserve the heat that is made and produce more heat if it is needed. First, a signal is sent to the muscle fibers around the blood vessels in the skin to constrict and decrease flow. This reduces a large amount of heat loss and warm blood is kept in the deep body areas. Skin temperature begins to approach that of the external environment.

If more heat is needed, internal metabolic rates are increased. A rapid increase in cellular metabolism is begun when the hypothalamus sends a nerve signal to the adrenal glands, which sit on top of the kidneys. A quick infusion of hormones from these glands, commonly called *adrenaline*, increases cellular "burning" of sugars to make heat. A slower process is started when the thyroid gland is stimulated with a subsequent release of thyroid hormone to increase overall metabolism.

Heat can be produced rapidly through an increase in muscle tone. By sending the right neurological signals, the muscle fibers rapidly pull against each another in an involuntary repetitive cycle known as shivering. In just a few minutes this process can raise the heat production rate to over four times the normal rate.

Conclusion

Incredibly, all of these processes working together keep a person's core temperature within 2°F of the set point over a 24-hour period. People groups also have some innate genetic capability to adapt over several generations to different climates through selection of variable traits such as basic metabolism, skin color, subcutaneous fat thickness, and behavior modification.

The information for these traits and all of the thermoregulatory process could never have been built up gradually through some long evolutionary route of trial and error. For survival's sake, thermoregulation has to be 100 percent in place and functioning. This process incorporates nearly every system in the body—which themselves have to be fully functional. The Lord Jesus' understanding of the human body He created and the magnificent complexities of His design are truly beyond description!

Balancing Body Temperature
Devotional Thought

So He came to a city of Samaria which is called Sychar, near the plot of ground that Jacob gave to his son Joseph. Now Jacob's well was there. Jesus therefore, being wearied from His journey, sat thus by the well. It was about the sixth hour. A woman of Samaria came to draw water. Jesus said to her, "Give Me a drink." (John 4:5-7)

The Lord Jesus knows the hardships that people face, even what it is like to be tired, hot, and thirsty. He willingly made Himself subject to the very intricate thermoregulatory system that He had designed and needed to replace water that He had lost during the hottest part of the day. Yet, in this setting He was still providing for the ones He had made, for He offered to the woman a "gift of God" if she would ask. He would give her "living water" that would be a "fountain of water springing up into everlasting life" (John 4:10, 14). What a tremendous gift that is available to anyone who will believe on the Lord Jesus as Savior! For those who have that gift of living water, remember to thank the Lord for that, as well as the physical water, the next time you are hot and needing a drink.

Questions

1. If an engineer was assigned a project to design a temperature regulation system, what kind of features would he have to design that are also found in the same system for the human body?

2. If someone became overheated on a hot summer day, they may experience symptoms such as muscle cramps, nausea, rapid pulse, headache, rapid breathing, and initially sweat profusely, but later feel just hot and dry. This condition could progress in a life-threatening situation. Based on information about how the human body offloads heat, what actions could be taken to help this person?

3. Given the wide ranges in temperature that occur throughout a year and even within a single day, a warm-blooded creature like a human could succumb to temperature extremes that could quickly lead to death. Why does this fact pose a problem for the slow, iterative evolutionary explanation for the thermoregulation system?

Answers

1. An accurate sensor must be sensitive enough to detect actual temperature changes located where temperatures are critical, like inside and outside a jet engine, and it must have a way to transmit the data, a computer for monitoring the data and comparing it to some type of standard, feedback controls, and a method to monitor rates of change so adjustments can be made before problems arise.

2. The body will try to lose most heat through the skin by conduction and evaporation—so increase contact with cool objects, replace lost water, and keep the skin moist so that this moisture can also be evaporated away. First, have the person lie down out of the heat and call for emergency assistance. Give cool fluids such as water or sports drinks (to replace the salt that has been lost); salty snacks are fine, but only if the person is alert and able to tolerate these. Loosen or remove clothing. Apply cool water to skin, wrap in a damp sheet and fan air across the skin and sheet, or, if very hot, place in a cool tub of water and monitor continuously. Do not use an alcohol rub or give any beverages containing alcohol or caffeine. It would also be a good assignment to look up what actions should be taken if a person were to get too cold, a condition called *hypothermia*.

3. This process shows integration of precise overall control from the central nervous system with innate information, like the body's core temperature "set point" already programmed within. Of course, this information would not be useful without respiratory, muscular, neurologic, endocrine (hormonal), and cardiovascular systems to execute the protective measures,

like sweating and shivering, that are necessary before death occurs. Even learned behaviors, like putting on clothing and seeking shelter, take too long to develop and become internalized in the population before extinction would occur. So, a slow process of accumulating enough beneficial mutations in DNA for all the systems to work together does not make any scientific sense.

Notes

_____

_____

_____

_____

_____

_____

_____

_____

_____

_____

_____

_____

_____

_____

_____

_____

_____

_____

_____

_____

_____

_____

Notes

_____

_____

_____

_____

_____

_____

_____

_____

_____

_____

_____

_____

_____

_____

_____

_____

_____

_____

_____

_____

_____

_____

[handwritten: Light energy + H_2O + CO_2 + plants]

[handwritten: Complexity of conversion of plants as food to useful energy in humans? $H_2O + CO_2$]

4
From Solar Energy to
Human Energy

P lants use biological systems that harvest light energy
from the sun to convert environmental water and carbon dioxide into tiny carbon/hydrogen energy units
stored within them. When people eat those energy
units, the extraordinary human digestive and metabolic systems
convert the work of plants into energy that is useful to people
and give back water and carbon dioxide to the environment that
can be used by plants. How do these systems make that happen?

Journey to the Stomach

Ingested food encounters precisely shaped teeth that cut
and grind it into small pieces—which, surprisingly, is the second step of the digestion process. The first vital step involves
the brain readying the digestive organs for an influx of food.
When the brain's "association areas" match smells, sights, and
even sounds of food with imprinted memories of eating, the
nervous system signals the process to start. Glands in the mouth
respond by secreting saliva, which is mostly water, but also
contains digestive enzymes, antibodies, and enzymes lethal to

some bacteria. Very sensitive chemical and mechanical receptors respond to even trace amounts of food by triggering a larger release of saliva—which is rarely in short supply, as salivary glands are capable of producing over a quart per day. Glands under the tongue make a sticky substance called *mucin* that the tongue mixes with chewed food and saliva into a sticky wet ball (a bolus) that can be easily swallowed.

After swallowing, an automated sensory-muscular system surrounding the esophagus senses the exact location of the food bolus. Simultaneous signals are sent to two different muscles: a contraction signal to a muscle closer to the mouth above the bolus, and a relaxation signal to a muscle closer to the stomach below the bolus. As the bolus moves below the relaxed muscle, it contracts and a still lower muscle relaxes in a coordinated rhythmic action that squeezes the food toward the stomach. The propelling force is strong enough to move food along the esophagus regardless of body position, even when it's upside down. A similar system is used in the intestines (with the addition of constrictive muscle zones that act as one-way valves to stop backflow of materials) to keep things moving smoothly there as well.

Breaking Food Down

The bolus arrives in the stomach, a sack-like organ with outer layers made of a huge number of elastic fibers laminated to a tri-layer of muscles: one layer with an oblique orientation of cells, one circular, and one longitudinal in the outer wall. Elastic fibers allow food to fill the stomach from the normal empty volume of about one half of a cup to hold over a gallon, if really stuffed. The orientation of the muscles allows the stomach to do the necessary churning of food to physically break it down and not just squeeze it into a tight ball.

Once inside, over a dozen important enzymes, hormones, and other factors are added to the mix to continue breaking down components, help capture nutrients, and activate other digestive organs at just the right time further down the process. Parietal cells secrete a very acidic concentration of hydrochloric acid (pH about 2.5) with a hydrogen ion concentration 100,000 times higher than in blood. Food is ground and dissolved into fine paste, but the stomach itself is protected from this harsh environment by an inner blanket of goblet cells joined very tightly to each other to contain the acid. These cells also secrete a bi-layer protective coat of sticky syrup-like mucus overlying a fluid which has a dissolved substance in it similar to antacid tablets that is capable of neutralizing any acid penetrating the top layer. The cells are programmed to be in a continuous state of renewal, resulting in a new inner lining on average every four days.

Nutrient Absorption

To optimize nutrient absorption, both the rate of stomach emptying and the type of enzymes added to the mix are initially custom-tailored to the types of food ingested by a part of the small intestine, the duodenum. Able to sense ratios of fat, protein, and sugar content, as well as the volume of food, the duodenum modulates a control valve exiting the stomach by a tandem of neurologic and hormonal networks. A regular meal is emptied in about four hours, while a high fat meal may be delayed an additional two hours or more.

The intestine is also protected from self-digestion with a coating of the lumen similar to that of the stomach. In addition, many digestive enzymes that would destroy the digestive organs themselves if they were in direct contact are really "two-part" enzymes. Similar to many industries using hazardous chemicals, these enzymes are kept in harmless-inactive forms by the pancreas until released into the safety of the lumen. An activator chemical made by cells lining the lumen is secreted into the lumen and transforms the inactive enzyme into an aggressive digestive form. This activated enzyme then acts like an activator to "turn on" other inactive enzymes in a coordinated digestive cascade.

Possibly the most impressive feature of the small intestine is its incredible surface area. If all of the folds and microscopic villi were smoothed out flat, the area of an average person's small intestine would cover over 1,500 square feet. This results in a capture of nearly 100 percent of all potentially absorbable nutrients. The final products are single molecules of glucose, amino acids, and glycerol broken down from carbohydrates, proteins, and fats respectively. These are distributed by the blood and lymphatic systems to all of the cells in the body.

Generating Energy

Many of these "raw materials" will be used to build new body tissues, but about 60 percent will be metabolized or "burned" to supply energy needs. At rest the average person will need to generate the equivalent energy to continuously power a 120-watt light bulb; heavy work can drive the power demand up ten-fold. But instead of electrical energy, body cells capture the chemical energy released when one molecule of adenosine triphosphate (ATP) is broken down to adenosine diphosphate (ADP). ATP is the universal energy currency of the body that special organelles of cells called *mitochondria* are constantly making from ADP. How?

Take a glucose sugar molecule that once existed as some of the starches in wheat bread before digestion. Glucose is composed of carbon, hydrogen, and oxygen atoms. Through three extraordinary processes involving dozens of enzymes, coenzymes, electron carrier proteins, and intermediate products, the atoms are stripped off the molecule.

One process uses the carbon portion to make ATP. The electron transport process uses the hydrogen atoms. Special proteins pump these atoms to one side of a hydrogen-impermeable membrane, while at the same time splitting the hydrogen into a positively charged proton and an electron. The flow is controlled in a stepwise fashion so that ATP is generated at several steps. Just like water behind a dam is released slowly through turbine generators, so the electron pairs are released slowly rather than all at once—which would only generate heat. But instead of gravity being the driving force to add energy, oxygen, which has been breathed in and carried by red blood cells to the mitochondria, is the driving force.

The attractive energy of one negatively charged oxygen atom strongly pulls two proton-electron pairs to eventually make one molecule of water and simultaneously pumps a high concentration of hydrogen ions across the membrane. Now an electric potential of energy has been established across the membrane. A current of hydrogen ions flows from "high" side to "low" side back across the

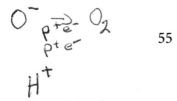

membrane, but only through special channels called *ATP synthases*. ATP synthases are actually tiny three-part rotary motors consisting of a rotor, a connecting rod, and an enzyme-embedded knob. In a process that converts electrical energy to chemical energy, these motors combine ADP and phosphate molecules by running them through gear-like structures to make ATP.

ATP is now available to power the needs of everything from muscle cells to neurons in the brain. ATP is not stored but continuously made and utilized. In one day, a person will make the equivalent of half their body weight in ATP.

From Sunlight to Body Power

In this amazing process that powers the human body, nuclear fusion energy in the sun is converted and conveyed as light energy to the earth, where it is captured and converted by plants to foodstuffs, then digested by a person and metabolized to universal energy packets that can be converted to chemical, mechanical, and electrical energy as needed. The information content behind all of this is truly staggering. The conversion of sunlight to body energy involves *all* systems of the body, plus a few plant systems, which must be totally functional. Credit belongs to the Lord Jesus Christ—the creative genius! The Lord is gracious to all people by freely giving the sun's light energy, the vital biological systems of plants, and humans' incredible digestive and metabolic systems.

Jehovah Creator God should be able to be known by all the things He created — His brand on them. PTL.

From Solar Energy to Human Energy
Devotional Thought

And saying, "Men, why are you doing these things? We also are men with the same nature as you, and preach to you that you should turn from these useless things to the living God, who made the heaven, the earth, the sea, and all things that are in them, who in bygone generations allowed all nations to walk in their own ways. Nevertheless He did not leave Himself without witness, in that He did good, gave us rain from heaven and fruitful seasons, filling our hearts with food and gladness."
(Acts 14:15-17)

After Paul had healed a lame man at Lystra, many in observance thought that he was a god and would have offered sacrifices to him. But Paul immediately pointed them to the one true God who is the Creator. It is interesting that Paul challenged the people that they should know that there is a God from the things that He created, but also by His good providential care and provision for His creation. Paul often told others that the Creator was the Lord Jesus Christ. We now know some of the intricacies of how the sun functions and how, through many incredible systems, energy is used by people. Those with eyes to see these truths are astounded at His ability to make such incredibly complicated and unified processes, which rightfully leads to thanksgiving and praise to the Lord Jesus.

Questions

1. Precise timing and coordination of different parts that work together toward achieving a specific outcome are hallmark features of things that have been designed. Identify several characteristics of the human digestive system that demonstrate precise timing and coordination.

2. The digestive system itself is made up of the same components that are in the process of digesting (a lot of proteins and some fats and carbohydrates). What protective features does the human digestive system have that enable it to do its job without digesting itself? What does the fact that these features exist say about a slow gradual process of minor successive changes as an explanation for their origination?

3. The metabolic system is not really a single system. Name some of the systems that must operate together in order to get solar energy to human energy. Do the interactions of these systems show any type of unity or "ecology" between humans and the rest of the world?

4. What is different about ATP synthase from an enzyme that is used to build protein structures? Why is ATP synthase such a different type of evidence for supernatural design?

Answers

1. The brain first associates smells, sights, and sounds of food with eating and sends signals to glands in the mouth to secrete saliva; chemical/mechanical receptors first sense food and then trigger a large release of saliva; muscles in the esophagus show precise coordination to constrict and relax so food is pushed to the stomach; different layers of stomach muscles allow food to be mechanically churned so as to be broken down.

2. The stomach is protected from dangerous hydrochloric acid (pH about 2.5) by an inner blanket of goblet and epithelial cells joined tightly to each other to contain the acid. Goblet cells secrete a bi-layer protective mucus overlying a fluid that is capable of neutralizing any acid penetrating the top layer. The cells are rapidly replaced on average every four days. The intestines are protected by similar cells and linings. Potentially dangerous enzymes are released in a form that is initially inactive and travel harmlessly to a site that is capable of safely containing the enzymes where they are combined with another substance to activate them. Without these features, the digestive system would become self destructive, which would be fatal. The digestive capability and the protective features must exist simultaneously and could not have evolved through a bit-by-bit, part-by-part process.

3. Actually, all of the body's systems are brought together to function as part of the metabolic system. But some of the more prominent systems are neurological, cardiovascular, respiratory, muscular, and digestive. The system in plants called the *photosynthetic* system, which makes carbohydrates and a few others that make fats and proteins, should also be included.

The human metabolic process is, therefore, a perfect example of unity in nature or ecology. (Ecology is the scientific study of living and nonliving processes that influence the number, range, type, and interactions of organisms and how organisms use or transform energy and matter.)

4. ATP synthase is one of several tiny molecular machines in the human body. They are called machines because they have several moving parts that must be built in a specific order and fit together precisely just like man-made machines. Similar to engineered machines, if one of the parts is missing or broken, the whole machine stops working. This demonstrates that all of the parts need to be present at the same time in order for it to work. ATP synthase is able to convert a constant flow of protons to a specific chemical energy that cells use.

Notes

Notes

_____

_____

_____

_____

_____

_____

_____

_____

_____

_____

_____

_____

_____

_____

_____

_____

_____

_____

_____

_____

5

Melanin, the Sunblock That's Just Skin Deep

Handwritten annotations: "Complexity of control of sunlight on the human skin" with "(Sun's raw energy)" above

Most people north of the equator have an observable suntan by August. Ironically, a desire to be outside is often coupled with another strong desire to get out of the sun, as indicated by sales of sun umbrellas and other types of sunshades.

From a biological standpoint, energy from the sun *always* needs to be controlled. This means that there is complex biological machinery in place to manage sunlight in some way. The machinery itself would not exist without information in DNA prescribing its materials, manufacture, and operation. Suntans result from this special biological machinery and function like the skin's own built-in umbrella to get skin cells "out of the sun." The process is so important that if it were absent, people would have a higher probability of being killed just by the sun's raw energy.

The Sun's Energy Damages Skin

The highly vulnerable top layer of skin—the part that is

tough, can callous, and eventually flakes off—is made of the protein keratin, produced by cells called *keratinocytes*. Sunlight—especially the ultraviolet (UV) part of the light spectrum—is naturally a photocarcinogen. It can penetrate keratinocytes, damage the DNA, and lead some cells to possibly be transformed into cancer cells, such as a deadly melanoma. The cumulative effect on the human species of sun-damaged DNA over time is not trivial. Humanity's survival is highly dependent on a mechanism to manage sunlight and repair damaged DNA. People produce a complex compound called *melanin* that dissipates the damaging effect of UV light as heat and helps prevent skin cancers in other ways also—but only up to a point.

Colored pigments in house paint protect the house's siding from sun damage. Melanin is a colored pigment for people, one of several compounds giving skin its coloration, generally contributing shades of red, brown, or black. Melanin is produced by *melanocytes*. Everyone has roughly the same number of melanocytes—regardless of skin color—but they are concentrated differently in various body parts to meet specific needs. There are over one million per *square inch* on the highly sun-exposed back of the hand, compared to 440,000 per square inch on the palm. Melanocytes produce different types and quantities of melanin based on inherited genetic instructions *and* dynamic gene regulation in response to a person's changing environment. This determines each person's skin color and allows the skin to respond to harmful UV light.

Melanin Can Control Harmful Energy

Melanin is contained in small packages called *melanosomes*, literally "dark bodies." The pigment melanin is not distributed randomly throughout the top layer of skin cells, the keratinocytes. Since it is particularly DNA in the skin cell nucleus that needs protection, it would make sense to place the melanosomes as a tightly packed shield, or protective sun umbrella, over the nucleus. That umbrella arrangement *on the sunny side* of the nucleus is exactly where the majority of melanosomes are found. With continued sunlight exposure, even more melanosomes are built and packed on the sunward side of the nucleus, sometimes several layers thick. Since a person can accumulate hundreds of millions of melanosomes per square inch protecting skin cell nuclei, the whole skin appears increasingly darkened, a condition popularly known as...a suntan.

So how does melanin protect the nucleus? There are two main steps. A fast step is produced by UV light itself, which induces melanin to undergo a chemical reaction that turns it darker. This enables it to absorb even more UV light. (Chemical engineers are working to develop paint pigments that can automatically change shades.) The second step is to stimulate melanocytes to produce more melanin. Consider this cellular relationship: one melanocyte can "serve" many skin cells by making melanin to protect their DNA and, in like manner, skin cells serve melanocytes by providing their vital protective covering.

How Melanin Is Produced

There are at least six major routes to stimulate melanin production. Melanin has other functions in the body not related to UV protection. But *all* routes require very strict control by several protein enzymes, and if *any* of these enzymes in the path is missing, melanin will not be produced. Eventually these routes all stimulate a messenger (called cAMP) that is able to achieve activation of genes in the nucleus of melanocytes to make more melanin. UV light acts as one stimulus.

Another stimulus is quite amazing. Under average sun-exposure conditions for a person, the *rate* of skin cell DNA damage and repair (an *especially* complex process) varies within a narrow range. Melanocytes indirectly monitor the repair rate, and if it rises—indicating increased sun damage—melanin production is boosted to protect DNA from further damage. Managers call that solving *the root cause* of the problem and not just fixing the consequences.

A melanosome is actually an *organelle* in a cell. This means it functions inside the cell with a definite purpose just like an organ, such as a kidney, functions in a body. But melanocytes are regularly making brand-new melanosomes. A melanosome is initially constructed of a fiber-like network foundation laid down by special protein (Pmel17) unique to melanocytes. To this is added a light-sensitive pigment called *L-DOPA quinone*, which is manufactured through a multi-step process from the amino acids phenylalanine or tyrosine.

The transfer of melanosomes from melanocytes to skin cells is unique in human biology, requiring a whole organelle specific to one cell type to be transferred to a completely different type of cell. How? The melanocyte will form long arms that will extend up between the skin cells. Growing inside are *microtubules* (so small that 3,000 could fit in the diameter of a human hair), which act like railroad tracks to shuttle melanosomes. Tiny protein motors made for the microtubules pull the *evolutionary speculation!*

melanosomes outward. Under the direction of at least two more genes and controlled by four carrier proteins, the melanosome is put into a transfer vesicle at the tip of the arm. This tip fits into a special invaginated spot on a skin cell, and then the melanosome is injected into it. Skin cells will convey melanosomes to the sunward side of their nuclei.

Interestingly, the varying *number* of melanosomes in both melanocytes and skin cells alters, in a measured degree, their metabolism and activity. This is one way in which the body's response to the environment can be centrally monitored at the cellular level in the tissue that is most exposed to external stresses. Melanosomes also can manipulate interactions of many compounds such as electrolytes and neurotransmitters and thus regulate the activity of other cells in its local environment.

Conclusion

Naturalistic evolutionists claim that because Earth is "open" to energy from the sun, life could have started and increased in complexity without a Creator. This notion is scientifically incorrect. As illustrated in human skin, raw energy from the sun must be *managed* by *preexisting* complex biological systems or else it kills life.

This fact of nature still reigns over all evolutionary speculations. In 2009 about 68,000 cases of melanoma were diagnosed, with an estimated one million reported and unreported new cases of mostly curable basal cell and squamous cell skin cancer—predominantly in lighter-skinned Americans. Melanin certainly provides a measure of natural protection, but nobody is immune from skin cancer, regardless of skin color. When people overexpose or fail to protect their skin, or have a defect in the pigment-making process, the sun's UV energy can eventually overwhelm skin's protective and repair mechanisms with deadly results.

The Lord Jesus Christ put the human body together to function as a whole. With unsurpassed scientific genius, He designed a complex process—using many different systems—that is capable of generating the protective compound melanin. With power beyond comprehension, He spoke into existence something that requires almost a hundred genes directing hundreds of enzymatic reactions controlling events—which are not arranged in basic linear sequences but as a vast diverse multidirectional network—with layers of overlapping feedback and control, all acting in a goal-oriented fashion. What an amazing display of His love and glory!

Melanin, the Sunblock That's Just Skin Deep
Devotional Thought

I am dark, but lovely, O daughters of Jerusalem, like the tents of Kedar, like the curtains of Solomon. Do not look upon me, because I am dark, because the sun has tanned me. My mother's sons were angry with me; they made me the keeper of the vineyards, but my own vineyard I have not kept. (Song of Solomon 1:5-6)

The dark skin of this woman was considered lovely by the Lord, who both inspired this passage of Scripture and created her. The physical qualities of all people, including outward appearance and skin color, is specifically chosen by the Lord (Exodus 4:11) and is an expression of His love for them just as in all things He created. The Lord Jesus enabled human DNA to be able to express a huge variety of physical traits pleasing to Him: people, therefore, should rejoice in this capability as well. The Bible says, "the LORD does not see as man sees; for man looks at the outward appearance, but the LORD looks at the heart" (1 Samuel 16:7). Placing little regard in outward appearance should be the model for human behavior. In reality, the extent of human variety is quite remarkable given the fact that the DNA of all people varies by less than one percent. Humans are actually far more alike than different, with similar wants and needs, especially everyone's need of a Savior for their sins. "For God so loved the world that He gave His only begotten Son, that whoever believes in Him should not perish but have everlasting life" (John 3:16).

Questions

1. The Bible teaches that when the Lord made the first humans, Adam and Eve, they did not wear clothes (Genesis 2:25). This would indicate that their skin had a lot of sun exposure. Why do humans today have to worry about too much sun exposure and why was it not a problem for Adam and Eve?

2. Melanin does a good job of protecting DNA from sun damage. Are there any other uses for melanin apparent from just observing a human body? Is it possible for melanin to have other uses that were of primary importance in the past but now are of lesser importance?

3. Control of melanosome production was said to solve "the root cause" of a problem. What does this mean in terms of DNA?

4. Given that keratinocytes (skin cells) do not make melanin but nonetheless need it, and melanocytes may have initially made melanin for purposes other than DNA protection of keratinocytes, how do evolutionists explain the important relationship between these two cells?

Answers

1. The first humans did not originally live in the same world conditions in which people live today. After Adam and Eve disobeyed God as recorded in Genesis 3, the Lord cursed all of nature. Many things in nature—probably as a direct result of genetic changes made by the Lord—became threatening or harmful to humans and animals. In addition, atmospheric and other changes resulting from the worldwide Flood of Noah's day (Genesis 6-9) have radically altered the environment even more. So now the whole creation suffers along with humans (Romans 8:19, 22) and is awaiting the return of the Lord when it will be set free from the curse.

2. Melanin has several uses in humans. Some are at the biochemical level that cannot be observed. However, what can be observed are different shades of color of body parts that are mostly due to different concentrations of melanin in those parts. These different shades highlight features that create a certain amount of diversity, interest, and beauty from both part-to-part and from person-to-person. It is quite possible that these functions for melanin were the primary functions in the past, but now due to changed environmental conditions, a protective function for melanin has become most important.

3. If DNA is being damaged from UV rays, one way to keep cells from possibly transforming into cancer cells would be to just increase the rate and thoroughness of DNA repair. However, this is like treating the symptoms of a disease. Physicians know that it is always better to prevent the disease—the root cause—rather than fix its problems. In like manner, increased melanin

production tends to work to prevent the DNA damage in the first place.

4. Random mutations (mistakes in DNA sequence) are the raw material from an evolutionary standpoint for all changes in structure and function. In order to gain some survival and reproductive advantage, an unknown common ancestor and its descendants over long periods of time would have had to have a series of mutations that: enabled melanocytes to indirectly monitor DNA repair rate in keratinocytes and adjust melanin production accordingly; formed long arms between the skin cells; developed a system of microtubules and tiny protein motors to service the arm; and possessed genes for four carrier proteins and a transfer vesicle at the tip of the arm. At the same time, skin cells needed mutations to induce the special invaginated spot that matched to the melanocyte arm and allowed melanosome to be injected into it. When the details of which mutations are actually needed to get things to function biologically are known, the evolutionary explanations are implausible.

Notes

Notes

6
Bone, an Engineering Marvel

The complexity of the human skeletal system, with its ability to remodel & maintain.

A key design feature shared by many 100-year-old barns and some modern skyscrapers is that the external shell carries the building's load with a minimal use of internal columns for support. Internal floors and walls, if any, function in a structural way to stiffen the building. This resourceful design allows for a very strong structure with a maximum of interior space available for other purposes.

The bones in the human body capitalized on this design feature long before farmers and architects did. In fact, studying bone construction and function provides a mini-course illustrating important engineering principles.

Sophisticated Engineering Properties

A quality product begins with materials that have superior engineering properties. Bone is constructed much like reinforced concrete, in which a cage of steel reinforcing bars (rebar) is embedded. The reinforcing "rods" in bone are made from minute strands of *collagen* fibers, 360 of which could be put end to end in the width of a human hair.

Each fiber is composed of three substrands wound in rope-like fashion around each other so tightly that along the area of contact only the smallest amino acid would fit in the space between the strands. In order to work, this particular amino acid would need to be designated for every third position in each strand—which is exactly what is specified in the DNA code. Collagen fibers are linked so strongly that their resistance to being pulled apart in tension is actually greater than the resistance present in an equal amount of steel rebar.

The bone's equivalent of the cement/aggregate part of concrete is composed of *apatite*. Apatite is a medium-hard mineral with properties similar to marble and is found widely distributed in rocks. A microscopic view shows that individual apatite crystals are bound to the collagen fibers and linked as a continuous mesh—but at full size the structure appears solid. Compared to reinforced concrete, bone is more *flexible* and has more *strength* to resist crushing compressive loads. This is vitally important, since a man lifting a 70-pound box actually exerts a normal compressive load of over 500 pounds on one of his vertebrae—just imagine the loads of Olympic weightlifters.

An important area of engineering research is designing materials that are *fatigue resistant*. Fatigue is a progressive failure due to the localized and cumulative damage that occurs when material is subjected to cyclic loading. Counteracting this is imperative, since in one year each hip bone for the average person will sustain about 1.8 million cyclic loads. Bone is one of the most fatigue resistant materials known due to its unique blend of strength, stiffness, and flexibility.

The actions of *bending* (compression/tension) and *torsion* (twisting) on bone are at their highest within the external shell. Dense-compact bone, able to resist these actions, is built into the shell. Inside, a three-dimensional network of small boney material resembling a porous sponge, called *spongy* bone, is found throughout small bones and at the ends of long bones. Spongy bone absorbs shocks and also contributes inner bracing or *stiffness*. The thin bony inner bracing elements do not grow randomly, but look and function like the support struts in the Eiffel Tower. Some studies demonstrate that if engineers apply a stress-strain analysis to a cross section of bone, it reveals that the boney braces are built along lines of maximum stress relative to the mechanical forces applied to them.

Fundamental Engineering Principles

Engineering *efficiency* strives for designs that completely fulfill an intended purpose while using minimal resources. Engineers can only dream of highways so efficient that they automatically expand from two to four lanes with population growth and contract with declines. In contrast, bone size does constantly change in response to demand throughout a person's life.

This highly efficient process called *remodeling* ensures that more bone is built in specific locations when it is subjected to heavy-repetitive loads and less is built when it carries lighter loads. In infants, 100 percent of the calcium is exchanged in their bones every year. For people in their 20s, the equivalent of 20 percent of the skeleton is replaced yearly—though high stress areas like inside the head of the upper leg bone may be replaced up to three times per year.

Remodeling also functions as a nonstop *maintenance program* for bone by tearing out old bone and replacing it with new. Concrete or block walls would last for ages if they had an outer covering that could continuously replace weak spots, repair cracks, or swap out rusty rebar. Remarkably, bones do possess such a covering.

The *periosteum* is composed of two important layers. The thin, lightweight outer layer consists of very flexible but extremely *tough* high-tensile-strength fibers akin to high-performance membranes that are now being utilized to wrap new buildings. The inner layer is composed mostly of two different types of cells kept in delicate balance—one type destroys bone and the other builds bone. These crucial cells are the workhorses for remodeling. The entire layer adheres tenaciously to the bone by means of strong, perforating fibers that embed in the collagen-apatite matrix. The concentration of these fibers varies and is appropriately very dense at spots where tendons connect to the bone.

A *robust* object withstands a lot of harm but continues functioning as intended. Sometimes the best response to a destructive force is to flex rather than to offer direct resistance. Automobile makers design "crumple zones" of materials intended to fold up or shear apart so crash forces are absorbed rather than transmitted to occupants.

Bones resist fractures in similar fashion. At the smallest level of collagen fibers, not all of the bonds are fixed solid. Some, called *sacrificial bonds,* are weaker bonds intended to break upon impact. Their exact arrangements in bone absorb and then disperse many forces that could rapidly reach the fracture threshold. But unlike a car's crumple zone, a bone's sacrificial bonds can repair themselves after the trauma, making them ready for another strike.

Damage Repair

Bones do have structural limits and can succumb to fractures that range from hairline to fully displaced. The cleanup and repair of bone exemplifies a thoughtfully engineered construction plan. A major fracture tears blood vessels, causing extensive bleeding and tissue swelling (pain results from torn or compressed nerves). Fortunately, blood eventually clots around the fracture, starting the healing. Within 48 hours, cells invade the blood clot and use it as a template to build a microfiber meshwork that acts as the "scaffolding" supporting the rest of the repair work. Other prerequisites to proper healing include broken bone ends being brought close together, aligned properly, and immobilized, with a sustained blood supply and the area kept free of infection.

The fracture zone is full of bone fragments and dead cells. Cells specialized in tissue demolition dismantle unusable bone fragments into their component parts. Other cells engulf and digest tissue debris. Valuable recyclable materials are saved and actual wastes carried off in the bloodstream to be discarded.

Man-made splints support fractures to prevent large damaging movements, but the broken ends still need further stabilization. Certain cells, called *fibroblasts*, work off of the "scaffold," laying down collagen fibers to span the break. Once some of the collagen bridge is made, new cartilage can be placed concurrently around the fibers. Fibroblasts will transform themselves into *chondroblasts* to produce this cartilage. Once built, the collagen-cartilage unit functions as new inner rebar, forming material (controlling the shape and location of the new bone), and the temporary bracing—all in one package.

83

Bones are living tissue and need to be nourished. Inside bone is an ingenious system of microscopic canals that comprise a thoroughfare to shuttle nutrients. Bone-building cells have multiple slender arms that radiate out from the cell body. When new bone is made, hundreds of these cells join their arms together to form a three-dimensional network that will become the basis of the canal system.

These cells will actually build new bone all around themselves and thus become entrapped within the bone. In essence, the cells not only make boney "concrete," but amazingly become their own forming material for the interior canals. With its job making bone now complete, this cell transforms itself into a nourishing/pressure-sensor cell called an *osteocyte*. Repair and remodeling processes make bone so resilient that in time a repaired bone may look almost identical to the original.

Conclusion

Bone structure is an engineering marvel. For its stress environment, it achieves nearly maximum mechanical efficiency with minimum mass, which designers call an *optimized* structure. Thus, bones remain a testimony to the genius of their Creator, the Lord Jesus Christ. In fact, bones are such an important feature in human design that they will remain with us for all eternity in our resurrected bodies, as Jesus demonstrated for His disciples (Luke 24:39).

Bone, an Engineering Marvel
Devotional Thought

And He said to them, "Why are you troubled? And why do doubts arise in your hearts? Behold My hands and My feet, that it is I Myself. Handle Me and see, for a spirit does not have flesh and bones as you see I have." When He had said this, He showed them His hands and His feet. (Luke 24:38-40)

The structure of bones gives strong evidence for their supernatural creation. The Bible makes it very clear that their Creator, the Lord Jesus Christ, rose *bodily* from the dead, had a real body after His resurrection, and is even described by the apostle John as still having a body in the future (Revelation 1:14-16; 19:11-16). To some of His own disciples who were unsure of His resurrection, He instructed, "Behold My hands and My feet, that it is I Myself. Handle Me and see, for a spirit does not have flesh and bones as you see I have." His resurrected body is a spiritual body not subject to the same limitations as a mortal body (John 20:26), but it is a *real* body. His body will forever bear the marks of our redemption and His triumph over Satan, sin, and death. Believers should also be encouraged because someday He "will transform our lowly body that it may be conformed to His glorious body" (Philippians 3:21), when the soul and spirit are finally reunited with a perfect body fully capable of serving the Lord.

Questions

1. If a person is in an accident or has a disease that destroys a joint, what engineering principle is most likely to be of concern to biomedical engineers that design replacement joints? What joints in the body do you think are some of the hardest to develop suitable replacement materials?

2. Is the fact that bones and joints wear out or are susceptible to disease an indication of bad design?

3. In humans, there is the set of fused, tapered, rounded bones, 4-5 in number, that articulate with the sacrum called the *coccyx*. Many evolutionists believe that the coccyx is a vestigial set of bones equivalent to the tail of many mammals. What does "vestigial" mean? Is the coccyx a vestigial set of bones in humans? Why would evolutionists refer to the coccyx as vestigial, and can they prove such an assertion?

4. The fact that bones demonstrate so many engineering principles—the application of which is always a challenge and goal for intelligent human engineers—would appear to be a very convincing argument for an intelligent origin for the structures in bone. How do evolutionists explain the existence of these engineering principles in bone?

Answers

1. Probably the biggest challenge is to develop materials that are fatigue resistant—that is, to not fail when subjected to possibly over a million cycles of rapid loading and unloading. The hip bone's curved shape at the neck, coupled with the number of cycles it must withstand, make it challenging. The temporomandibular joint, where the jaw bone (mandible) articulates with the temporal bone of the skull, is also a challenge because the joint is small and subjected to very high pressures every time a person chews food.

2. Joints and bones break or wear out, but this is no more evidence of bad design than the fact that even the most complicated devices designed by humans also wear out and breakdown. The main question is do structures in the human body show the same features of design as in man-made devices? To that question, the answer is a resounding *yes*. Evolutionists attribute design features to "apparent" design. This means that they acknowledge that things look designed, but there was not really an intelligent agent doing the designing. Creationists attribute design features in the biological world to an Intelligent Designer, the Lord Jesus Christ, which is what evolutionists and creationists both do when observing design features in non-biological areas.

3. "Vestigial" is an adjective describing an organ or part that is greatly reduced from the original ancestral form and is at the present time a remnant of the primitive structure and no longer believed to be functional or important. The whole concept of declaring an organ to be nonfunctional because its function is not known is totally counter to the inquisitive, questioning spirit in which science should be conducted and tends to

chill research on supposed vestigial structures. In addition, it is essentially impossible to prove an organ is nonfunctional. The pronouncement of the coccyx as vestigial is particularly egregious since people have been dissecting human bodies for centuries and its function is very obvious. The coccyx is vital in helping support muscles and other tissues that make up the pelvic floor, serving as a primary attachment site for the external anal sphincter muscle (keeps the anal canal and orifice closed). In addition, the interior surfaces work as important attachments for muscles that help contain feces within the rectum and that aid the delivery of babies during labor (the coccyx can also rotate back during this process). Because evolutionists are firmly committed to the belief that humans descended from an ancestor with a tail, this belief remains the driving force to declare the coccyx a vestigial structure—"tail bone"—in spite of its important current functions in humans.

4. If evolutionary literature could document a mechanism for developing these design features or show a transition of creatures where these design features came into existence little-by-little, that would be a good argument against Intelligent Design. But these facts are not found in evolutionary literature. Instead, design features are observed as fully functional in skeletal structures that are fully suitable for survival purposes in the creature in which they are found. The standard answer that is given is that "nature has had millions [or billions] of years to perfect the design." (Look this phrase up on the Internet and see how many times it is repeated—even in prestigious scientific journals.) This explanation appears to be completely unchallenged in peer review. Of course, this is not a scientific answer at all, as it is overly broad and not testable. That is why this type of phrase is not found in engineering and medical scientific literature.

Notes

_____

_____

_____

_____

_____

_____

_____

_____

_____

_____

_____

_____

_____

_____

_____

_____

_____

_____

_____

_____

_____

Notes

_____

_____

_____

_____

_____

_____

_____

_____

_____

_____

_____

_____

_____

_____

_____

_____

_____

_____

_____

_____

_____

7
Immune Systems, the Body's Security Force

The Complexity of the human body to identify and resist "foreign invaders" — defend.

Good neighborhoods provide families a lot of protection, but even the best of communities remain vulnerable to the threat of criminals invading their homes. Our human bodies are also vulnerable to foreign invaders such as bacteria, viruses, fungi, and parasites. But when these infection-causing microbes break in where they don't belong, they face a serious defense force, eventually to be caught and destroyed by a highly trained, cell-sized army equipped with a sophisticated array of weaponry. That security force is called the human immune system. Designed with amazingly dynamic communication networks that pass information back and forth between hundreds of millions of cells, the human immune system strategically fights off microscopic invaders and remembers them each time they attack the body.

Without this defense system, none of us could survive, much less reach maturity. When the immune system becomes weak due to disease, immaturity, or deterioration, death is far more likely from infection or cancer. Medical intervention attempts to keep the immune system intact, but little help can be offered once it collapses

Preparing the Immune System for Conflict

Like any conflict, the first priority must be to distinguish friend ("self") from foe ("non-self"). Cell surfaces are covered with hundreds of protein markers differing in type and combination. One very important marker, the MHC1, is on almost every cell (except red blood cells). Like all proteins, DNA specifies its makeup. But MHC markers are special. The possible genetic combinations as to exactly how it will "look" are so large that *no two people* have the same combination (except possibly identical twins). As cells recycle materials, this marker actually takes tiny portions of their unique cell fragments and displays these on the surface. In the womb the immune system is "programmed" to recognize self by learning, in a sense, what these surface markers look like. Immune cells programmed to recognize self reside in the lymphatic and blood systems. Their color is grayish-white not red, so they are called the *white blood cells,* or WBCs.

New generations of WBCs start forming in bone marrow. Specific hormones in the marrow or the thymus gland control programming so knowledge of self is passed on. This is important because WBCs operate on only one creed—any marker on any surface that is not totally self is non-self and will be attacked and destroyed. Markers play a pivotal role throughout the process. Non-self obviously includes bacteria, viruses, fungi, parasites, and toxins like snake venom. One's own cells may be included if infected *inside* by viruses or internally transformed by cancer. If so, portions of these non-self proteins are carried from inside and placed on the cell surface by the MHC. This, in effect, marks its own cell for destruction.

How Microbial Threats Are Identified

Hundreds of millions of microscopic invaders that trigger defensive immune responses are collectively called *antigens*. Among the WBCs, T cells and B cells are the key players in mounting very specific responses to threats and then keeping these in memory. Once these cells mature, they not only recognize self but will express a receptor that will bind primarily to *one* type of antigen. Each of these cells may have over 200,000 receptors on its surface. The process controlling maturation—colloquially called "cellular boot camp"—is exquisitely selective. If T or B cells fail to recognize their specific antigen or show any reactivity *against* self, they are tagged with proteins prompting self-destruction. About two percent of manufactured cells make it through boot camp. These cells have not yet been exposed to antigens so they are "naïve" to their threat. They are sent to lymph nodes, other tissues, or simply circulate waiting to be exposed. Exposure for some is almost immediate, while others may never be exposed.

Since T or B cells make well over one billion different receptors, some researchers assert that *no* environmental threat exists for which a matching receptor has not *already* been made. So humans are not passively waiting for invading microbial antigens to determine which receptors will be made. Rather, the body has cells ready to meet any antigen that arrives. Some cells even have receptors for antigens that have never existed in nature. This incredible inventory of receptors is specified by genes in DNA, yet the total number of genes currently identified in humans is about 26,000. Actually, T or B cells in the boot camp only use a few hundred genetic bits of information, but these are controlled by an

95

elaborate process that shuffles segments, allowing an astronomical number of combinations. One receptor region determines its classification and allows it to interact with other cells. Another region is variable and will "fit" to some antigenic marker that initiates identification and the attack.

Microbes commonly invade through the mouth, lungs, or broken skin. Anticipating the invasion are millions of cells called *antigen-presenting* cells (APCs), which are strategically located in places like the tonsils or just under the skin. APCs constantly sample anything entering the body, and invaders are killed, their cells are broken apart, and many tiny portions—the antigens—are carried by these APCs to lymph nodes and "presented" to T or B cells. T cells that "fit" the antigen become activated. Some T cells may also run into APCs on chance encounters while circulating in blood. A race begins the moment an invader enters the body. Many microbes reproduce rapidly, so the body must destroy them while they are fewest in number.

Activating a Specific Immune Response

Activated T cells initiate immediate and wide-ranging responses. At least 20 different chemical signals are sent throughout the body. Some attract "helper" T cells, "natural killer" cells, "cytotoxic" T cells, and other WBCs to home in at the site of infection. B cells are activated by these T cells, APCs, or directly by antigens. The chemical signals also drive many other important functions.

Activated B cells start reproducing lineages of exact clones. Most clones are directed to undergo dramatic internal restructuring, thereby becoming cells able to make an *antibody*—an extremely important protein for fighting infection. These antibodies have regions that "fit" to antigens via similar genetic shuffling mechanisms as its "ancestor" B cell. However, an intricate cyclical process ensures that the antigen-antibody fit gets progressively better by becoming even more specific. How? The B cell's genes prescribing variable regions have genetically unstable areas guided by a mechanism that fosters *hypermutation*—totally random genetic mutations resulting in very slight changes to variable regions from one lineage of antibodies to another. A few new antibodies will fit to the antigen a little better than others. Right on schedule, another type of cell takes the best fitting antibody-antigen package to a special location inside lymph nodes. The B cell making that antibody continues to the next cycle, while all other B cells that made less specific antibodies are sent a signal to self-destruct. After about six days of these mutation-selection cycles, thousands of cells will be making highly specific antibodies—and each of these cells manufactures antibodies at rates of about 2,000 *per second*.

Eliminating Threats

Invaders now face an extraordinarily fierce two-pronged attack. Antibodies may directly neutralize some threats like toxins, cause some antigens to clump together harmlessly, or most importantly, cover other microbes with thousands of antibody "bull's eyes" targeting them for certain destruction. Once microbes are marked as non-self, there are very few places to hide. Once found, immune proteins may attach to microbes and punch hundreds of holes in them, additional cells may split them apart, other cells may attach to them and inject substances causing them to self-destruct, and many more may engulf them and force them into internal "sacks" filled with acid, hydrogen peroxide, or bleach.

Toxins like those from tetanus bacteria or snake bites act so fast that ready-made antibodies from another person or a horse must be injected in victims to neutralize the toxin. More often, after someone's initial exposure to an antigen, a few B cells that made the most specific antibodies transform into long-lived cells called *memory* B cells. When memory B cells (and memory T cells) see that antigen later, the entire immune response revs up stronger and produces huge quantities of antibodies in just a couple of days. Vaccines are compounds containing portions of dead or weakened antigens to deliberately expose people and thereby get their immune system primed. Often-fatal childhood diseases like smallpox, measles, and polio have been greatly reduced with this strategy. A newborn's immune system needs developmental time, but is conferred good initial protection by antibodies from his mother that cross the placenta and from his mother's milk.

Conclusion

The immune system doesn't have even one central dedicated organ—it is a functional system dependent on every other body system, which themselves would not survive without immunal protection. It's a complex system, and every area fights selflessly to rid the body of its foe and cleanse it of deteriorated cells. The immune system's Creator, the Lord Jesus, is even more astounding. For "Christ also loved the church and gave Himself for her" (Ephesians 5:25). As typified in the immune cells He created, He too is mighty to save and protect His Body, even when acting to His own detriment.

Immune Systems, the Body's Security Force
Devotional Thought

Finally, my brethren, be strong in the Lord and in the power of His might. Put on the whole armor of God, that you may be able to stand against the wiles of the devil. For we do not wrestle against flesh and blood, but against principalities, against powers, against the rulers of the darkness of this age, against spiritual hosts of wickedness in the heavenly places. (Ephesians 6:10-12)

Just like in the microbial world where the threat cannot be seen directly by human eyes, the spiritual battles believers are engaged in cannot be directly seen—but they are just as real. The Bible makes it clear that a spiritual enemy seeks to oppose the work of Christians (1 Thessalonians 2:18), distort biblical truth (2 Timothy 2:25-26), hurt them (Luke 22:31), accuse them of sin (Revelation 12:10), or ruin their reputations (1 Timothy 3:6-7; 1 Peter 5:8). The believer does not resist these attacks with physical weapons but "with the sword of the Spirit, which is the word of God" (2 Corinthians 10:4; Ephesians 6:17). It was the Lord Jesus who defended Peter from Satan's attacks, and it is only the "Son of God [who] was manifested, that He might destroy the works of the devil" (1 John 3:8). Believers can confidently take refuge in the Lord Jesus during *any type* of battle, for He is a faithful and supremely capable defender of His own.

Key?

Do you "battle" against negative thoughts in your mind?

Questions

1. Darwin said that if it could be demonstrated that some organ could not possibly have been formed by numerous, successive, slight modifications, then his theory would absolutely break down. The immune system does not have any specific dedicated organ, but is more of a functional system. Is Darwin's concern about its development still valid? Why?

2. In what periods of human history was there an "arms race" between countries? Does an arms race imply that the technology of the competing countries is progressively getting better? Why do evolutionists use the analogy of an arms race to describe the conflict between microbes and other creatures?

3. A prominent evolutionist and expert in immunology, Edward Max, argues that the *hypermutation* process is a classic example of evolution in action. He argues that the supposed evolutionary process in nature that led to the diversity of life on Earth from one common ancestor (phylogenetic evolution) and hypermutation operate very similarly to each other. Is Edward Max's comparison scientifically legitimate? (See The Evolution of Improved Fitness By Random Mutation Plus Selection by Edward E. Max, M.D., Ph.D.; www.talkorigins.org/faqs/fitness/.)

Answers

1. Darwin's concerns would be even more applicable to the immune system. Since the immune system depends on every body system to be fully functioning to operate, the evolutionary problem of explaining the origination of *all* the body organs would apply to the immune system. The immune system is critical for the survival of humans (and other creatures as well). This clearly demonstrates a total body unity, or an all-or-nothing level of complexity that extends way past the molecular level all the way to that of the organism. Darwin's theory is still absolutely broken down.

2. The classic example of an arms race was between the United States and the former Soviet Union during the Cold War. Each country used increasingly better technology to build weapons better than the other side. Evolutionists support using the analogy of an arms race between creatures evolving immunological defenses and microbes evolving ways to get around them, even if this analogy is completely wrong. This analogy does give the impression of totally natural pressures propelling evolution in an ever upward and onward direction. Bacteria becoming resistant to antibiotics is a favorite illustration used by evolutionists. In reality, this resistance shows no evolution at all. In many cases the information for the resistance was already in the population of the strain of bacteria *before* the antibiotic was introduced. Mutation/natural selection combinations did not create it. It merely favored those bacteria that already had it. The fact that bacteria can swap segments of DNA between themselves only demonstrates an exchange of information, not the creation of new information. In other cases, resistance is conferred by a *loss* of a function

(the one that the antibiotic was using to get an advantage over the bacteria). These bacteria are actually *weaker* than the rest of their bacterial family not exposed to the antibiotic. Their only advantage is in the environment containing the antibiotic. Some cells in creatures also destroy function as a last ditch effort to protect themselves from invading microbes. Neither case typifies an arms race.

3. The process of increasing antibody affinity is not similar to nor mirrors phylogenetic evolution in any way that Darwin proposed, and most evolutionists understand it. There are several important differences between the two processes: 1) Increasing antibody-antigen "fit" (affinity) is *not* truly random, while the proposed natural process for phylogenetic evolution *is* totally random. 2) Increasing antibody affinity uses a specific mechanism with multiple enzymes and other cellular players to induce hypermutation. Phylogenetic evolution does not undergo hypermutation and, by definition, has no controlling mechanisms involved. 3) Increasing antibody affinity relies on another mechanism to cause competing B cells to kill themselves off. Phylogenetic evolution relies on natural selection to wipe out competition. This is not even remotely as efficient as automatic self-destruction for eliminating competition. In fact, most animals that do not breed in one season survive and may go on to breed in future seasons, thus keeping their genetic material within the population. 4) Increasing antibody affinity uses the *extremely precise* fit between antibody and antigen to apply "strong selective pressure" to increase affinity. Phylogenetic evolution cannot demonstrate any naturally occurring screen that applies to populations of creatures that is anywhere near as selective as antibody-antigen affinity.

Notes

_____

_____

_____

_____

_____

_____

_____

_____

_____

_____

_____

_____

_____

_____

_____

_____

_____

_____

_____

_____

Notes

_____

_____

_____

_____

_____

_____

_____

_____

_____

_____

_____

_____

_____

_____

_____

_____

_____

_____

_____

_____

8
Life-Giving Blood

The complexity of the human circulatory system, particular fluids, etc. [handwritten annotation]

After 100 years, automobiles still need engine oil, transmission fluid, brake fluid, antifreeze, power-steering fluid, and so on. Wouldn't it be great if just a *single* multipurpose fluid could be circulated from a central reservoir? Each part would use only the needed properties of the fluid, exclude detrimental properties, and then send it back. The new system's worldwide impact would ensure a huge market—and academic honors—for the clever developers.

This lucrative breakthrough, however, would not be pioneering. Just such a brilliant integration of fluid properties to the diverse needs of the physical body has already been achieved in human blood—in a self-starting process beginning about 15 days after fertilization.

Heart and Blood Vessel Formation

The first human cell divides rapidly, becoming a small cluster that implants inside the uterus. Initially it flattens out to a disc only a few cells thick that is able to get nutrients by diffusion from maternal blood circulation. However, by two weeks after fertilization the disc is becoming too thick for this, so the developing embryo urgently needs a nutrient transport system.

Right on cue, blood and blood vessel formation begin at the end of the second week in *both* the embryo and developing placenta. Heart tubes (the precursor to the heart) form and start pumping within seven days. The cardiovascular system is the first organ system to become functional—an important factor, since every cell depends on blood to survive.

Vital Characteristics of Blood

Blood is a *liquid tissue*. For normal human function, blood has to be a fluid. Why? Fluids can flow, carry either suspended or dissolved solids and gases, and respond to even slight pressure changes by continuously changing shape. Blood and blood vessels, therefore, form an incredibly flexible conduit—the exact shape of a person's body at any moment—that connects the outside world to the deepest cells inside. Cellular metabolic demands are relentless. That is why nearly all of the estimated 60 trillion cells in the body—each one carrying out an average 10 million chemical reactions *per second*—are always close to blood vessels bringing oxygen and fuel.

Blood is made up of solid (formed) parts such as oxygen-carrying red blood cells (RBCs), disease-fighting white blood cells (WBCs), and platelets suspended in a liquid that is 92 percent water. This liquid, called *plasma*, has about 120 dissolved components that include oxygen, carbon dioxide, glucose, albumin, hormones, and antibodies. Sensors continuously monitor the concentrations of these items and make swift adjustments. Vital body functions like normal acid-base ratio, intracellular water content, blood's ability to flow through vessels, and managing body heat production depend as much on correct concentrations as the correct mix of components.

Fetal Blood Production

The embryo makes RBCs first, his most necessary blood component. These distinctive cells are made by the inner lining of blood vessels in a temporary structure outside the embryo called the *yolk sac,* which in people is actually a "blood-forming sac" that never contains yolk. This misguided name was given because it was believed to have "arisen" in a pre-human animal ancestor and because it initially contains a yellow substance.

The progenitor RBCs eventually migrate from the yolk sac to the liver and spleen, which become the lead cell-forming sites by the mid-second month of gestation. By the fifth month, bone marrow is sufficiently formed to take over for nonstop lifelong production. Interestingly, even in adulthood if the body is stressed by a shortage of RBCs, the spleen and liver can resume production as emergency backup sites.

In children, blood formation occurs in the long bones such as the upper leg and shin. In adults, it occurs mainly in the pelvis, cranium, vertebrae, and sternum. However, development, activation, and some proliferation of certain WBCs occur in the spleen, thymus gland, and lymph nodes. Normally, sensor-control mechanisms balance mature RBCs from their production to their loss—which is about 1,200,000 cells *per second.* How does the marrow produce these prodigious numbers of cells?

Blood Formation: A Precisely Planned Process

Blood formation begins with a *self-renewing* population of *pluripotent* stem cells that are capable of developing into *any* type of blood cell lineage (RBC, WBC, or platelet). They reproduce by making exact copies of themselves called *clones* or *daughter cells*. Some daughter cells or originals remain as pluripotent stem cells, but the rest will be "committed" to specific lineage pathways. Which cells stay as stem cells and which get committed is a random process. In contrast, the survival and expansion of cells in each lineage is precisely controlled by dozens of interacting chemical signals called *colony stimulating factors* (CSFs)—some produced in other body tissues. CSFs control numerous activities, including turning certain genes on and off at just the right time so each unique feature of the cells is made.

The marrow provides a protected microenvironment where immature cells grow on a meshwork of fat cells, large WBCs called *macrophages,* and cells lining the marrow. The meshwork compartmentalizes the nurturing process and also secretes vital CSFs. Proper growth is stimulated by strict regulation, in stepwise fashion, over both order and timing of when 12 major CSFs are introduced to the blood cells. Controls are so exact that concentrations of CSFs from other tissues can be as low as 10^{-12} molar (like one grain of salt dissolved in about 27,000 gallons of water). Amazingly, at certain steps in the process some of the maturing (or mature) blood cells *themselves* emit CSFs to direct their own development or even control the meshwork.

For RBCs, a crucial stimulating hormone is *erythropoietin,* commonly called EPO. Without EPO, no RBCs would be made. EPO is steadily circulated, keeping RBC production at the normal rate. But "normal" for a 10-year-old girl at sea level may not be "normal" for a 60-year-old man living on a mountain. The genes with instructions for making EPO are controlled by stimulants known as *hypoxia-inducible factors* (whose function depends on several vital enzymes). These factors activate EPO DNA but *not* in response to the number of RBCs. Rather, low oxygen concentrations induce more EPO production, which normally results in rapidly rising RBC numbers. By regulating just exactly what is needed—the blood's ability to carry adequate oxygen—the optimum number of RBCs running at maximum oxygen capacity is continuously and efficiently adjusted. Therefore, it would be fitting for EPO to be produced mainly in an organ that is very sensitive to changes in blood pressures and oxygen content, such as the renal cortex of the kidney—which it is.

Integrating Blood Properties with Organ Function

The familiar biconcave shape of human RBCs bestows the highest possible membrane surface area relative to intracellular volume and oxygen saturation rate. This makes it possible for over 250 million hemoglobin molecules in each of the billions of RBCs to be oxygen-loaded in a fraction of a second. Recall that nearly all body cells are in close proximity to blood vessels. By necessity, most of these vessels are tiny capillaries, of which 40 could be put side by side in the diameter of a human hair. RBCs are twice the diameter of a capillary but can actually squeeze through it. How? Structural properties in the RBC's membrane allow the cell shape to be incredibly deformed and then spring back to normal. Five specialized structural proteins confer this important ability and a genetic defect in any causes diseases due to rupturing of less-flexible RBC membranes.

RBCs are themselves living tissues. It would be possible for RBCs to consume much of their oxygen payload with little left to supply other tissues. However, RBCs have enzymes to power their metabolic processes *without* the use of oxygen—so they consume none of their precious cargo.

Several kinds of cells, like the clear cornea and lens of the eye, need the oxygen and nutrients carried in blood but could not function properly if coated in red blood cells. This problem is overcome by a part of the eye that acts like a blood filter. Using ultrafine portals—so small as to screen out RBCs and other proteins—a crystal-clear, water-based portion carries just enough dissolved oxygen and nutrients. After nourishing the cornea, the fluid is reabsorbed—through another set of tiny holes—back into the bloodstream. Cerebral spinal fluid and urine are some other ultrafiltrates of blood in which only some of blood's properties are extracted to fill a need at a precise location.

Conclusion

From the earliest days in the mother's womb until the day of death, a person's life is in the blood. Even a person-to-person gift of blood is treasured and called "the gift of life." Human blood is indeed a gift from the Lord Jesus Christ, clearly testifying to His great creative abilities and the body's total unity of function. The Bible says that the Lord Jesus' blood is particularly special—in fact, "precious" (1 Peter 1:19)—because it is able to redeem us and cleanse us from all sin (1 John 1:9). Let us give glory "to Him who loved us and washed us from our sins in His own blood" (Revelation 1:5).

Life-Giving Blood
Devotional Thought

Not with the blood of goats and calves, but with His own blood He entered the Most Holy Place once for all, having obtained eternal redemption. For if the blood of bulls and goats and the ashes of a heifer, sprinkling the unclean, sanctifies for the purifying of the flesh, how much more shall the blood of Christ, who through the eternal Spirit offered Himself without spot to God, cleanse your conscience from dead works to serve the living God? (Hebrews 9:12-14)

One of the best evidences for the inspiration of the Bible is its absolute unity in message from cover to cover. A very clear message is that without the shedding of blood there can be no forgiveness of sins (Hebrews 9:22). Right after Adam sinned, the Lord slew animals and made clothes for Adam and Eve (Genesis 3:21), demonstrating the blood atonement. As noted above, the sacrificial system given to Israel required the offering of goats, calves, and other animals. Particularly poignant was the prominent role of blood on the annual Day of Atonement when the high priest would enter into the Holy of Holies, dip his finger in a bowl of blood, and sprinkle it on the Mercy Seat of the Ark of the Covenant. What glorious pictures these were of the coming sacrifice of the Lord Jesus Christ. But the blood of bulls and goats cannot take away sins (Hebrews10:4). Only the blood of the perfect Son of God has the power to completely purge sin, its condemnation, and the guilty conscience! The world may be offended by the blood atonement, but Christians stand forgiven in the fact that "the blood of Jesus Christ His Son cleanses us from all sin" (1 John 1:7).

Questions

1. The beginning of the chapter used an analogy of parts of an automobile that all use fluids. In what ways does blood serve to fulfill some of these same functions in a human body?

2. The process of blood formation makes a very strong argument for design. What aspects of this process could be emphasized to show that it would be highly unlikely for the process to have been formed by numerous, successive, slight modifications?

3. Engineers are regularly assigned projects whose final product must "be fit for an intended purpose" (this is the usual engineering, and legal, definition of a *complete* project after the contract clauses are satisfied). How does control of erythropoietin production fit this engineering goal and definition?

4. The cornea can be supplied oxygen without the use of RBCs. Why can't the same process be used in other tissues like muscle?

Answers

1. Fuel: blood carries sugars, fats, and proteins to tissues of the body that metabolize these to energy; power steering pump and conduits: blood pumped by the heart works like this to maintain adequate blood pressure to overcome gravity, fill certain organs and keep them rigid, and even maintain the pressure in an eyeball and keep its shape; engine coolant and radiator: blood is able to absorb heat from inside the body and carry it primarily to the skin and lungs where it can be off-loaded to a cooler outside environment. All of these systems in a car are designed and use specifically designed fluids. In the body, the properties of one fluid—blood alone—are able to meet all of these needs and more.

2. All of the following tissues are vital for the formation of blood, but cannot contribute to this process unless continuously supported by blood: 1) dozens of interacting chemical signals to precisely control the process of which some are produced in other body tissues; 2) genes and genetic controlling proteins that must be activated/deactivated at just the right time so each unique feature of the cells are made; 3) fat cells, large WBCs called *macrophages*, and cells lining the marrow to nurture the developing RBCs. In addition, maturing (or mature) blood cells themselves emit CSFs to direct their own development or even control the nurturing cells in the marrow. So, just like the formation of a baby in a mother's womb, it takes *developing* RBCs to get *developed* RBCs. Considering the absolute survival value of RBCs for a creature to live and reproduce, it is very unlikely that this process could be derived by numerous successive genetic mutations.

3. The primary purpose for transporting RBCs in blood is to carry sufficient oxygen to tissues so they can carry out their own purpose. By placing an oxygen sensor in a very oxygen-sensitive tissue like the renal cortex, how well blood is meeting its purpose can be monitored. The *number* of RBCs, in some respect, is irrelevant; what is needed is a certain amount of *oxygen content*. Since many factors affect oxygen content, the number of RBCs can be modulated to meet the body's needs for various conditions. The fact that erythropoietin is also produced in the cortex, which is responsible for acting like a throttle on a whole cascade of other processes vital in RBC production, again gives evidence that the body itself functions as an integrated whole.

4. The metabolic demands of the cornea are much lower than in most other tissues (particularly an oxygen-demanding tissue like muscle), so the oxygen requirements are much lower.

Notes

Notes

9
Complexity of the **brain and nervous system**

Throwing Darwin a Curve

"The pitch cuts the inside corner of the plate for strike two." That familiar sound is heard on radios around the world. In fact, some of the best pitchers in America are not Americans. Great pitching ability is not limited to ethnicity or geography, but rather to human beings alone. Great pitchers make it look so easy, and "practice makes perfect," but it helps that the brain power necessary for control, neurological connections, and muscular arrangements for the human arm are exceedingly better than *any* system that exists on the planet. Is throwing a ball really that complex?

Planning Motor Activity

Most people have heard of "grey" matter and "white" matter in the brain. If the brain were cut in half and viewed from the end, two distinct layers would be seen. The darker-colored outer layer of the brain, about one-quarter-inch thick, is the grey matter, and the white-yellow area inside is the white matter. In very broad terms, the grey matter associates sensory input with memories, plans motion and muscular activities, and provides awareness of sensations. It is called the *cortex* and is the conscious part of the brain. The white matter is composed of nerves that are covered in an insulating material with high fat content, giving it a whiter color. The connections are not random, but organized into "tracts" carrying data from one specific point to another. However, the number of connections is huge, so every part of the brain is essentially connected to every other part.

One part of the pitcher's cortex is the *premotor* area. Since childhood, the pitcher has been storing thousands of plans in this area that coordinate the actions of whole groups of muscles. It is the primary storage location in the brain for learned skills, particularly ones that are repetitious in nature. While every pitch is unique, the general plan for muscle coordination pertaining to each type of pitch is stored—and constantly refined—in that area. A great major league pitch was started possibly at age two when the pitcher was handed a ball by his father and he made his first toss, influenced by every throw since then. Today, the pitcher will pull a general plan for a curveball from the premotor cortex.

The premotor is absolutely essential to control muscular movements. Large muscle groups are controlled and coordinated so that simultaneous and ordered motions occur as planned. A pitch involves primary muscle groups in the neck, hand, arm, shoulder, trunk, hips, legs, and feet. Individual neurons send impulses to several muscles and each muscle receives impulses from neurons in multiple spots in the cortex simultaneously. Several neurons in the brain control each muscle, and each muscle is sent impulses from neurons located in several locations in the premotor cortex. This extent of control is necessary to achieve proper muscle coordination for pitching.

The batter is a power hitter, so the pitcher decides to throw the ball a little high and over the outside edge of the plate but still in the strike zone. From the moment of his decision, he will be modifying the premotor general plans. He fixes his eyes on his target. He knows that the path of the ball is going to follow an arc—not an absolute straight line—so he wants the end of the arc to be at the correct elevation. Hitting that elevation is primarily a function of speed and distance. Good pitchers have programmed these factors into the premotor area. But the exact elevation of any one particular pitch has not been programmed, so conscious changes to the plan are inserted. Wind and type of pitch also figure into the trajectory of the ball.

The rehearsed plan from the premotor area, coupled with conscious modifications, is sent to an adjacent area of the brain called the *motor* cortex and simultaneously to the *cerebellum*. This distinct area of the brain located toward the back and base of the skull functions like an extraordinarily rapid gatekeeper and a switching station. As a gatekeeper, it receives movement and environmental data from all of the sensors in the tendons, muscles, eyes, ears, skin, etc., and sorts out those pertinent to the execution of the pitch—an astonishingly huge number. It will couple that input with data from the motor cortex and send instantaneous modifications to the execution of the plan back to the motor cortex and to the muscles. As the pitch is performed, the motor and premotor cortexes and the cerebellum work in concert in a blindingly fast "circuit" that provides continuous input from the brain, through the spinal cord, then out through thousands of microscopic nerves to the muscles.

Integrating Visual and Vestibular Input

Looking back to the batter, even if the catcher has not moved his mitt to become a target, the pitcher can still lock onto a target of plain three-dimensional space. How? Subconsciously his eyes pick up cues regarding distance based on the relative height of the squatting catcher, umpire, home plate, batter, and other things. Keying on any movement of the people around the target, the relative motions one to another also give accurate indications of depth. These cues are constantly being compared with data stored in memory to give an extremely accurate estimation of distance relative to height or motion. Another aid is his "stereo vision" (since the distance between pitcher and batter is less than 600 feet). The pitcher's eyes are set about four inches apart. However, this small distance is enough to allow the line of vision from eye to object to not be parallel but angled. The slightly dissimilar images projected onto the retina are interpreted by the brain as a three-dimensional image that helps aid in the sense of depth or distance.

A right-handed pitcher's body will pivot on his left foot and rotate toward the left. To stay locked on target, his left eye turns toward his nose, the right turns toward the right temple, and they both rotate (to compensate for head's leftward tilt) a little to the right—in *exact unison*. Six small, extremely fast muscles for each eye control these movements.

As the pitcher turns through his pitching arc, the body's rotary motion is sensed by *semicircular canals* in both the left and right inner ears. The right semicircular canal sends an *inhibitory* signal to an eye muscle attached to the nose bone of the right eye and the temple bone of the left eye—which allows the muscle to relax. The left semicircular canal sends an *excitatory* signal—of exactly equal timing, magnitude, and duration—to an eye muscle on the nasal side of the left eye and the temporal side of the right eye, causing contraction. Visual input is integrated with these inputs and "tempers" these signals that contribute to extremely smooth eye motion fixated on the target while the head and body move around them. While the right hip of the pitcher may swing through an arc covering more than four feet, the eyes will turn through the same number of degrees of turn (generally until release of the ball) but move about one inch.

Meanwhile, tiny adjustments are being made to the circular motion of the arm, wrist, fingers, and trunk all the way down to his feet. The arm swings through an arc angled from the perpendicular, and at just the right time the wrist rotates so the hand stays in the same orientation toward the ground. Muscles in the forearm start to flex the wrist forward, moving it in its own small arc as the whole hand swings forward. The wrist's movement inputs spin to the ball and increases power. At just the right moment during the swing the brain sends signals to the muscles controlling the thumb. Pressure by the thumb on the ball loosens in a carefully graded manner. Promptly thereafter, muscles in the back of the arm are signaled to just barely loosen finger pressure on the top of the ball. The force imparted to the ball pulls it out of the hand at the right moment so its trajectory is right on target at over 90 miles per hour…for a strike.

Conclusion

Drawings of cavemen throwing primitive spears may seem convincing evidence of humanity's evolutionary ancestry for those who fixate only on the spear. This makes no more sense than standing in awe of a free-falling 500-pound "dumb" bomb but ignoring the stealth jet fighter that released it. For anyone not blinded by evolutionary prejudice, it is easy to see that the real star of the show is not the archaic spear—but the incredible *arm* that threw it. All arms reflect features of design whose origins resist natural explanations. In no small way, misplaced appreciation robs the Lord Jesus Christ of His rightful praise as the prestigious Designer. Yet, His arms remain open, inviting all to "come to Me, all you who labor and are heavy laden, and I will give you rest" (Matthew 11:28).

Throwing Darwin a Curve
Devotional Thought

Behold, the Lord GOD shall come with a strong hand, and His arm shall rule for Him; behold, His reward is with Him, and His work before Him. He will feed His flock like a shepherd; He will gather the lambs with His arm, and carry them in His bosom, and gently lead those who are with young. (Isaiah 40:10-11)

Strength and gentleness are put side by side in these two verses, highlighting that in the Lord these are not contradictory, just a contrast of two of His infinite ways. It is noteworthy that the arm is the symbol used to illustrate these two traits—even though God does not have arms. Because He used the picture of arms, which is something that everyone can identify with, He is teaching what people can also do with their own arms. Men should be particularly instructed since they can develop very strong arms and tend to have the more aggressive nature. The Lord Jesus Christ is a perfect model for all to follow, who used His strong arm to turn over the tables of the money changers and drive them from the temple (Matthew 21:12), yet gently took children up in His arms (Mark 10:16) and used His hands to heal (Luke 13:13). It is, of course, encouraging that regardless of how His people may fail in the use of their arms, the Lord never does. The reality of being gathered up in His strong arms and carried close to His heart should be a source of great encouragement.

Questions

1. Chimpanzees and human beings have very similar-looking but not identical arms. When observing chimpanzees, what is a capability their arms have that human beings don't possess?

2. Since humans and chimpanzees have similar arms, why is it that humans have such greater ability to control precise movement?

3. If a paleontologist unearths a stone spear tip or arrowhead, what does that artifact say about the mental capacity of its maker?

4. What do you think are the differences between these major muscle groups that control arm function: shoulder girdle, upper arm, and lower arm?

Answers

1. Chimpanzees have the ability to hang by their arms for long periods. They can also use their arms like legs, i.e., their knuckles and wrist bones are different from humans, allowing them to be used for walking.

2. The human brain has large areas dedicated to the motor cortex to exert control over the muscles allowing them to work in highly coordinated fashion. In like manner, a Cessna plane and a fighter aircraft have similar parts (flying surfaces) but very different performances. The fighter's more powerful engine does not make it superior; it is the ability to rapidly and precisely control the parts of either aircraft that allows one to fly at supersonic speeds and the other to dust crops. If you were to take the arm of a major league pitcher and surgically implant it to a chimp in place of its arm, the chimp would not be able to throw a major league pitch because the ability is not in the arm alone but in the control of the arm. Also, the inability of the chimp arm to exert the same precise control as the human arm does not mean that the chimp arm-brain combination is more primitive or inferior to the human arm (any more than human arms are primitive to the superior strength in the arm of a chimp). They are just different. Each one is designed to do what *best meets the needs* of each kind of creature.

3. The artifact "says" nothing. Many paleontologists discover artifacts and subsequently attach a story to the artifact that is a pure fabrication of their imagination. The very common story is that the primitive tool is the product of a primitive brain. This is incorrect. Tools are more indicative of the particular state of human discovery—or technological advancement—

Good point

130

than they are of mental capacity. There is no evidence that inherent mental capacity for human beings has increased in the last 200 years, yet the number of technological discoveries has dramatically increased.

4. Muscles tend to move the bones (on which they insert) across the joint from which they originate. The muscle groups of the arm fall into two categories: numerous smaller muscles guiding precise movements and fewer larger muscles for powerful movement. This is exactly what is found in the overall arm design. In order to move the arm in three dimensions, the shoulder has numerous muscles oriented so the whole arm can move in all three axes. Once in position, a set of opposing powerful muscles of the upper arm endow a strength capability for pushing and pulling—that is needed only in one axis. Another set of numerous smaller muscles in the lower arm provide the wrist and the hand with an infinite number of configurations. The shoulder enables your arm to be positioned and then allows options of 1) strong push-pull motion, 2) or less powerful but fine-tuned motion of the wrist and hand, 3) or both at the same time.

Notes

Notes

10

Complexity of speech

Created as an Instrument of Praise

I t can cut paper, saw wood, open cans, and loosen screws. It has small tweezers and even a toothpick. What is it? It's the ubiquitous Swiss Army knife—the forerunner of all hand-held versatile tools. This little red knife is so well known that other multifunctional items are often referred to as "the Swiss Army knife of…." But did you know that your body has its own amazing versatile tool? It's called the tongue, and it fulfills critical but diverse functions for eating, speaking, oral health, immune defenses, and many other areas. What makes this organ even more incredible is that it does all of these things with only two major types of tissue: muscle and mucous membrane.

Muscles of the Tongue

The tongue is not a single muscle but rather is composed of eight muscles. Four originate on bones in the neck, skull, or jaw. These muscles enable large tongue movements like pressing against the roof of the mouth or against the sides of the teeth, pushing food to the rear, or sticking it out through the lips. In spite of their small size, these muscles are very powerful but remarkably

135

agile. A significant amount of the motor portion of brain cortex is devoted to muscle movements of the tongue.

Four symmetrical pairs of muscles that originate in and insert on tongue connective tissue are intrinsic to the tongue. In order to optimize up-down, left-right, or elongation movements, tongue muscles need to be orientated in all three axes of movement. Each muscle on the right half of the tongue is paired to an identical muscle on the left half. Control is exquisite. Signals can be sent so that both work in tandem, such as lifting the tongue's tip, or work as mirror images, such as rolling the tongue. At times a stimulatory signal is sent to the right half and an inhibitory signal sent to the left, as when the tongue is bent to the right. The opposite happens when it is bent to the left. All intrinsic muscles can work to move the tongue into a specific shape while extrinsic muscles simultaneously move the tongue as a whole, changing its location.

The result is that the tongue's speed and movement combinations involved in speech—especially when coordinated with lip movements—are enormous. The average person speaks about one word per second. Professional readers of "fine print" for commercials read three to four words per second. But that's not even close to their fullest potential. Utilizing the inherent nimbleness of the tongue and lips, the brain can exert such control as to drive everything into speaking *10 words per second,* with each word being heard distinctly (analyzed with a high-speed recorder). To get an idea of the sensitivity of the tongue for speaking, consider its capability for material manipulation. Without the aid of eyesight, the tongue can flatten material into a uniform thickness, punch a hole in the center, roll it one way into a tube or roll it another way into an almost perfect sphere, and then shape it into a cube.

Membrane of the Tongue

The pink mucous membrane covering the muscles is another multifunctional marvel. One main purpose of the tongue is to successfully "grip" items that may be slippery, rough, or even sharp—while protecting in the process. Thousands of small nipple-shaped projections called *papillae* are arranged in neat rows and confer the tongue's coarse texture, enabling it to manipulate materials even covered in a super slippery substance called *mucus*. Unlike skin overlying other oral surfaces, tops of the papillae are covered with the same tough skin that is on the palms of hands. This thicker skin on top of the tongue is whiter compared to the sides. The durability of the skin is so protective, like that of a glove over a hand, it actually allows very gentle handling since it minimizes dangers posed by damaging food and teeth.

Embedded in the membrane are *taste receptors*—papillae of more complex structure able to sense different chemicals. Though tending to cluster in certain locations, they are found anywhere on the top surface (except one type found only toward the back of the tongue). These papillae are like a castle surrounded by a moat or trench. The trench catches exceptionally tiny fragments of food material where receptor cells sample its chemical composition. When 50 to 150 of the receptor cells are grouped together in the trench they are called a *taste bud*. Receptor cells have one primary taste stimulus: sweet, salty, umami (a meaty protein taste), sour, or bitter. However, receptors possess a wide range of responses to their primary stimuli, and there is appropriate overlap. Since chemicals are very responsive to temperature, cold and hot foods themselves can stimulate different tastes and influence the intensity of those tastes. One obstacle to overcome is that many chemicals are by nature very erosive, resulting in considerable wear and tear to the receptor cells. To meet this challenge, taste bud receptors are replaced on average every eight days.

A bite of food activates hundreds of different sensor cells. Thousands of signals sent to the brain—which can be mixed in essentially unlimited combinations—are interpreted within the brain as "flavors." Feedback gives the sensation that the taste is in the mouth, but the brain is actually doing the tasting. The brain's tasting center sends signals to other locations in the brain where flavors are linked to emotional responses. To some extent these can be trained (hence the vastly different reactions by children worldwide to a spoonful of cod liver oil), but others appear to be "hard wired" in the brain. Tests on newborn babies, before any exposures to food, confirm they smile when challenged with sweet tastes and grimace when given bitter tastes—indicating that in humans these senses are present from birth. In other tests the average female has a keener sensitivity to taste than the average male in all age groups and across cultures. Unfortunately, the sensitivity to both taste and smell begins to decline after the age of 60 for most people.

Close to the junction of the tongue to the mouth's floor is a series of ducts secreting saliva from sublingual glands. This saliva is mostly water for lubrication, but about 2 percent of it is the stringy-sticky mucus. Saliva also plays a critical role in oral hygiene. To minimize oral infections and tooth decay, sublingual saliva contains 1) a specialized class of antibodies suitable for secretion, 2) antibacterial enzymes, and 3) compounds that act like a localized antibiotic.

The posterior one third of the tongue (a special mirror is

needed for viewing) is covered with *lingual tonsils* that serve as a sentry outpost for the immune system. Specific cells in the tonsils "sample" the materials coming in through the mouth and rapidly alert the body if noxious organisms are entering.

Combined Ability of Muscles and Membrane

The dexterity of the muscles coupled with the characteristics of the membrane give the tongue almost "hand-like" capabilities dedicated to the care of the mouth. The ability to correctly identify two points in close proximity, light touch, thermal sensations, texture recognition, and tastes is the highest ability of any organ in the body. The tongue can easily sense foreign objects—even a single wisp of cotton—in the mouth, which signals an almost irresistible nagging urge to remove it. When the brain is able to visualize the shape of an item, without benefit of sight, by means of manipulation, it is called *stereognosis.* The tongue is second only to the hand in its ability to discriminate between complex objects based on shape, size, weight, temperature, and texture. Most people are able to maneuver an unseen object in their mouth and then precisely draw it out by hand. Or, if the object is familiar to the person, they can *identify* it, though it may never have been handled with their tongue previously. This ability is so precise that physicians can use it to try to detect neurological abnormalities.

Conclusion

The presence of a tongue does not make us human, but in many ways the tongue becomes the avenue through which actions entirely unique to humans are expressed. It is control of the tongue coupled to its innate physical abilities that bestows capabilities to fulfill diverse purposes. Evolutionists assert the fact that both humans and many animals possess tongues is evidence of common ancestry. This claim reveals shallow biological analysis in that it completely misses the crux of the issue—explaining the origination and organization of all the components of *any* tongue. "Nature" did not provide humans with a tongue. It was a gift from the Lord Jesus Christ that enables people to express love for each other in poetry, song, and other ways. Even more importantly, it enables a verbal avenue to honor the Lord in appreciation for what He has created, just as David did: "I will praise You, for I am fearfully and wonderfully made" (Psalm 139:14).

Created as an Instrument of Praise
Devotional Thought

And they sang a new song, saying: "You are worthy to take the scroll, and to open its seals; for You were slain, and have redeemed us to God by Your blood out of every tribe and tongue and people and nation, and have made us kings and priests to our God; and we shall reign on the earth." (Revelation 5:9-10)

That is a glimpse of how the tongue will be used in the future; but in our present age, people struggle. The tongue has been called "the most powerful muscle in the body." Anybody who has been "beat up" by one can tell how much a tongue lashing can hurt. Even small people can bully with their tongues, and everyone has been a bully at some time. The Lord Jesus said, "For out of the abundance of the heart the mouth speaks" (Matthew 12:34). The tongue is the avenue for expressing bitterness, rage, envy, and a whole lot of other evil. Sadly, when people don't get their way, and particularly when their feelings are hurt, they can turn loose the most harmful words on the people they love the most. James said, "And the tongue is a fire, a world of iniquity" (James 3:6). While all creation is exhorted to praise the Lord (Psalm 150), it is only by the Lord's life-renewing power that the tongue can be totally different. Many Scriptures tell of how our tongues, reflecting changed hearts of believers, confess the greatness of the Lord and delight in praising Him. David declared, "And my tongue shall speak of Your righteousness and of Your praise all the day long" (Psalm 35:28). But one use of the tongue is certain for everyone. Paul said of the Lord Jesus, "That at the name of Jesus every knee should bow, of those in heaven, and of those on earth, and of those under the earth, and that every tongue should confess that Jesus Christ is Lord, to the glory of God the Father" (Philippians 2:10, 11).

141

Questions

1. The tongue in creatures is very similar to the neck—very common but also very different in shape and function from creature to creature. What are some differences in tongue use for a chameleon and an anteater? What animal has the fastest-moving tongue?

2. What are some ways the use of a tongue is different for animals than for humans?

3. What are some of the ways recorded in the Bible where the tongue is used to express a type of human emotion?

Answers

1. A chameleon is a reptile and an anteater is a mammal, but both have very long tongues (almost one half of their body length) and both are used to trap food. The chameleon uses a very sticky tongue that it can extend very rapidly and accurately to catch its prey. Not only does it need a long sticky tongue, but also the neurological and muscular parts to control it. Without all of these parts, chameleons, as real science knows them, could never use their tongue for hunting. The anteater allows ants to climb onto its tongue. The ants are removed after the tongue is retracted. The tongue has protective features to keep it from being injured by biting ants. The animal with the fastest tongue is the giant palm salamander of Central America. It can shoot its tongue out to about one half of its body length in 7/1,000 of a second.

2. Humans use the tongue as a method for heat removal, though it is not a major organ for this function. Humans could use the tongue for cleaning, but aside from fried chicken that is "finger lickin' good," there is no instinctive tendency for this. Most humans lack the ability to wrap their tongue around things and pick them up. However, all of these actions are commonly used by many different animals.

3. Praise, sing, shout, laugh, cry, curse, blaspheme, spit, and several others are found in the Bible. There is even a record in Scripture of people sticking out their lips as a way of showing disgust but not their tongues (Psalm 22:7). The fact that people can use their tongues to verbally commune with God is part of being made in the image of God (Genesis 1:26). This is

a great gift; but the use of the tongue, like other things (Exodus 34:26), can be perverted to the exact opposite of its intended purpose.

Notes

Notes

The Complexity of the Human abilities of the human hand.

11
The Connecting Power of Hands

Aboom in affordable housing in the 1950s was helped by the invention of a distinctive multifunctional piece of equipment: the backhoe. Its strong yet relatively slender articulated arm allowed precise yet rapid placement for digging or lifting. The manipulative device is trim and fast, since hoses transfer power to it from a powerful hydraulic pump within the main chassis.

The "arm" of the backhoe makes many people think the equipment design is similar to a human arm, but what makes it so versatile is that it is actually more like a giant human finger. If a valuable piece of equipment mimicking just one finger can be so useful, what capability is possible in a real human hand?

The Formation of Hands

That capability begins as an embryo reaches the end of the fourth week of gestation. A special patch of tissue on the budding limbs stimulates invading cartilage cells to become templates for future bone. Other signals induce muscle-forming cells to develop a muscle mass in the arm and hand. These masses auto-

149

matically subdivide into 12 muscles of the forearm that act on the wrist and fingers, and 19 intrinsic muscles of the hand that manipulate only fingers.

The hands are initially flat plates, with the cells making vital internal structures of fingers. The skin cells between fingers undergo a programmed cell death, allowing the formation of five separate digits arranged in the uniquely human hand pattern— right from the start. Muscular ability develops fast. By 16 weeks an embryo can firmly grip a small rod, and at six months the fetal grip is so tight that he can be lifted by it.

Finger Flexing

To curl fingers, forearm muscles on the front pull tendons attached to finger bones while muscles on the back concurrently relax. The reverse happens to straighten them. Both groups can pull simultaneously, working with intrinsic muscles, to hold fingers stiff.

Functions depend on coordinated control and on component arrangement. The tendon to the finger's middle bone actually splits apart and allows the tendon for the bone on the tip to pass through the center of it. This allows the fingertip to flex independently while keeping both tendons tight to the finger bones.

Compared to animals, human behavior with hand tools is fundamentally distinct. Exclusive elements of hand movement are attained *only* when the unique human hand's muscular configuration and the brain's disproportionately large hand sensory and motor function centers *are integrated together*.

Grip: Manly or Microforce

The most important element of hand movement is *opposi-*

tion, meaning the ability to squeeze (such as between fingers and thumb or palm and fingers). While some weightlifters generate "bone crushing" grips, an average man's grip is a respectable 100 pounds of force. To grasp something, people must subconsciously or purposively control three acting forces for the object, three tendencies for it to twist on an axis, and six mechanical variables for *each* finger (such as degree of participation).

Massive investments in brain capacity with direct projections to many hand muscles means that grip control combinations are infinite and remarkably versatile. A construction worker can easily take one hand and curl three fingers around a bucket handle in a looser "endurance grip," while the thumb can press a note card tight to the index finger and the pinky can hook a plastic sack. At the same time, the other hand can curl the last three fingers and press the palm firm over their fingertips locked in a "power grip" to carry a heavy hammer, while the thumb and index finger gently pluck up a potato chip without crushing it.

When it comes to either passively detecting or making extremely small movements, the fingers may be great, but the human thumb is extraordinary. This is due to a forearm muscle called the *flexor pollicis longus* (FPL), whose tendon independently bends the thumb's tip. The FPL is not present in chimpanzees, gorillas, orangutans, or monkeys.

The human brain employs exquisite muscle motor commands over the FPL, especially at low levels of effort. Individual muscle fiber units can be recruited—in order—by very low rates of nerve stimulation to generate a finely graded thumb-tip twitch force of only 7/100 of an ounce. The same muscle units pull double duty as sensors to accurately estimate magnitudes of extremely low forces against the thumb—which underpins the

151

superior accuracy of the thumb for highly skilled tasks requiring a "precision pinch."

Fine Finger Movements

Fine manipulation is possible using just the fingertips. This results primarily from combining muscle actions of seven muscles that actuate the index finger, five major muscles unique to the thumb, and even three additional muscles dedicated to the pinky finger. Besides movement, the muscle-tendon networks of the fingers also store a measurable quantity of elastic energy that is monitored—independent of the nervous system—by analyzing how much the tendon network is deformed. Nonlinear mathematical computations, made at the cellular level to describe the network in a type of sophisticated "body logic," act like power switches to regulate force production. This means hand muscles can be directed to perform like hydraulic rams, springs, or even force-dampening devices in just the right situations.

In addition, a seamless "muscle-sensor" continuum combines the muscle data with additional neural input on information such as spatial position and pressure from fingertips, nails, and fatty portions of the hand. The fingerprint structure of elevated curved and straight parallel skin ridges is an exquisite sensor that functions like a piece of corduroy fabric in which the ridges provide contact sensation but the directional nature of the fabric in each ridge is detectable.

This degree of control is vital to handling things using just fingertips, since fingertips must rapidly transition from three *mutually incompatible* actions to pick up objects—motion toward it, abrupt contact with it, and then an increasing but precisely directed isometric force against it. Mathematical models

152

show that the brain devises a time-critical *predictive* strategy that enables massive neural-muscular patterns to swap out the fingertip actions from "movement" to "pinch" in only about 60 *milliseconds* (about 1/6 the time it takes to blink an eye).

The brain calculates exactly how long to hold back executing the strategy so that fingertips start flashing through their movement changes about 65 milliseconds right *before* contact. High speeds are attained as the nervous system controls only task-relevant muscular parameters but allows task-irrelevant ones to fluctuate. Neuromuscular control is so optimized that performance approaches the physical boundary of a hand's capability. Recall this the next time your fingertips squeeze to crack an egg with about 10 pounds of force and abruptly stop within the distance of the shell's thickness—about 1/100 of an inch.

Finger Speed and Forward Planning

Human finger movements excel in precision and *speed*. The average time a person takes to make a common choice between two things is about half a second. But rapid finger motions are much faster—in fact, even faster than is physically possible using only the body's sensor-to-motor loops. To obtain the highest possible finger speeds, sensors and conscious thought are augmented in the brain with an anticipatory function for individual finger movements called a *forward plan*, which is extraordinarily complex and significantly subconscious. Evidence shows that the central nervous system predicts the best outcome of every finger movement *several movements ahead* of its current state.

Thus, skilled typists will visually process up to eight characters in advance and then—in anticipation—the forward plan for muscle movements will commit the finger muscles to an action about three characters *in advance* of actually striking the keys. Times between keystrokes are commonly as low as 60 milliseconds. Interestingly, speed is fastest if successive keystrokes are between fingers on opposite hands.

So imagine the quantity of mental data processed for a skilled pianist who can play 20-30 successive notes with each hand every second—about 40 milliseconds apart—since the nervous system executes a forward plan (prescribing speed, direction, pressure, duration, etc.) for *every* finger *simultaneously* and updates all plans after *every* successive finger movement. The plan is compiled in the cerebellum, which may, if needed, retain memory of the plan (one or several varieties). This becomes an integral part of skilled learning. So far, no limits have been found on the number of plans that can be kept in memory.

Conclusion

The astounding performance of human hands allows them to excel in an even more powerful way—hands connect. Hands are a main avenue to express creativity and feeling (including conveying language), are the primary apparatus to implement a person's will, and coupled with eyes become the principle sensors for self-awareness. Thus, they are a vital link to connect a person's inner immaterial spirit to their physical body. They can connect a person to a loved one with a caress and then to the rest of the world—mostly through work.

It is altogether fitting for the Lord Jesus to use the skill, strength, and awesome connecting power of hands to express His love. He promises that His hand will guide (Psalm 139:10), uphold (Isaiah 41:10), and faithfully keep His own in His powerful grip (John 10:28).

The Connecting Power of Hands
Devotional Thought

Now when Jesus had crossed over again by boat to the other side, a great multitude gathered to Him; and He was by the sea. And behold, one of the rulers of the synagogue came, Jairus by name. And when he saw Him, he fell at His feet and begged Him earnestly, saying, "My little daughter lies at the point of death. Come and lay Your hands on her, that she may be healed, and she will live."
(Mark 5:21-23)

The incredible power of the Lord Jesus was often expressed through His hands. Of course, anything is possible by the expression of His will alone and in other instances by His spoken word (John 11:43). When He used His hands, He made a tangible connection between Himself and another person, which was an unmistakable token of His heart—predominantly, compassion and love. Later in Mark's account, He took Jairus' daughter, who had died, by her hand and restored her to life. In love, He did not raise His own hands when Roman soldiers smote Him with their hands (John 19:3) as part of His suffering under the direction of leaders who used their "lawless hands" and had Jesus "crucified, and put to death" (Acts 2:23). As testament of His payment for the very sins of those wicked hands, He now bears "in His hands the print of the nails" (John 20:25), but these are now in triumphant resurrected hands that are alive forevermore.

Questions

1. The chapter describes a mass of muscle tissue in an embryo that self-divides into distinct muscles, and the skin between fingers undergoes a programmed cell death in order to form five separate fingers. Explain why evolutionary theory is unable to fully account for the origination of embryonic development itself.

2. If a person suffered trauma to their forearm, how might this affect their hand? Tell what "opposition" means and what ability it confers. If the trauma happened to the thumb, what ability may be reduced?

3. Explain how today's teenagers are able to text-message each other at very fast speeds. Is it possible to "overload" the messaging system?

4. Name several ways hands are used to connect a person's body to their emotions. What are some ways a person can connect themselves with others that can honor the Lord?

Answers

1. Evolutionary theory is based on random genetic mutations leading to the development of biological processes and structures through numerous, slight, successive modifications passed on from ancestors to descendants over many generations. The major problem with this theory when it comes to embryonic development is that the information needed to make an embryo—necessary for a continuing lineage—must be present as the embryo develops, or the embryo will never develop. Without this information, no living embryos, for humans or animals, would ever survive. No organism would be subject to natural selection and thus evolution could not even get going. Listen and look for conjecture words like "maybe," "might," "could have," and "possibly" during the next encounter with an evolutionary explanation on the origin of embryonic (or any other area) development. These are not words of scientific tentativeness or doubt, which is useful in science, but words that cover huge gaps in plausible scientific explanations and link one improbable evolutionary story to another.

2. Depending on the severity of the trauma, some finger control may be partially or permanently lost because there are multiple muscles in the forearm that act on the wrist and fingers. The thumb may lose some of its function; it is controlled by the forearm muscle called the *flexor pollicis longus* (FPL). "Opposition" is the ability to squeeze and is the major component of a person's grip. The thumb has the best ability to detect or make extremely small movements.

3. The brain uses anticipatory function for individual finger movements called a *forward plan*. Teens texting messages

acquire rapid finger movements similar to the way a skilled pianist learns to play music. Even though there is no known limit to the number of plans that can be stored in memory, the activity of executing plans demands a level of attention usually *proportional* to the complexity of the task being performed. Even very smart, highly skilled, and practiced fighter pilots can get "task saturated" with trying to fly the aircraft, talk on radios, navigate, watch controls, track radars, monitor threats, and plan their attack. The fact that so many of these skilled tasks can be done well is a testament to the incredible computational capacity of the human brain. However, many accidents result from aircraft operators being overwhelmed with too many things to execute simultaneously. Most people, particularly teens, have not developed multitasking skills, and that is why they should never try to text and operate any type of machinery at the same time.

4. Actually, almost any body part can be used to convey an emotion, and people who have lost their hands do find other avenues of expression—but hands do it best. Many activities can be done to honor the Lord if they are done for His glory. Some that emphasize hands are people skilled in sign language that translate audible messages for the deaf, instrumentalists performing music, or missionary surgeons removing a cataract or repairing a cleft palate—and sharing Christ with their patients.

Notes

Notes

_____

_____

_____

_____

_____

_____

_____

_____

_____

_____

_____

_____

_____

_____

_____

_____

_____

_____

_____

_____

12
Human Reproduction

Complexity of (handwritten) via Sex (handwritten)

A new life is started the moment a human sperm cell unites with a human egg. Sounds simple, doesn't it? A person can decide for himself, but he will need to follow along very closely to catch all of the details and carefully piece them together, just as he would follow a skillful mystery.

The voyage of a single sperm cell from production to fertilization begins with rapidly dividing cells within a testis called *spermatogonia*. These divisions are crucial to place in the sperm cell 23 chromosomes—exactly half the number within normal human cells. When the sperm fuses with the egg, which also has undergone divisions within the mother's ovary, the full complement of 46 chromosomes will be present. However, cellular mechanisms allow slight variations in the information contained on certain portions of the chromosomes to be shuffled during the divisions. This feature ensures that each sperm and egg carry the correct information to make a normal human, but each is different as to the exact traits that will be expressed by the new person. The genetic combination in the newly fertilized egg will be totally unlike that of any person who has ever lived before or ever will be born afterward—truly resulting in an absolutely unique individual.

The sperm starts out as a round, immobile cell. It is surrounded by other cells in the testis called *Sertoli cells,* which function only to transform the sperm cell into a lean swimming machine that is capable of carrying its genetic cargo to the egg. Sertoli cells transfer nutrients to the developing sperm from the blood stream, since at this point in development the sperm must not be in contact with blood. Large amounts of cellular fluid within the sperm called *cytoplasm* are also removed by the Sertoli cells, and internal cellular components are precisely rearranged so that the sperm begins to take on the shape of a long and slender cell with a whip-like tail. An important structure, the *acrosomal body,* that will eventually develop highly erosive enzymes—able to dissolve the membranes around other cells— is made by Sertoli cells at the newly developed head of the sperm and sealed in a protective coat.

A high concentration of the male hormone testosterone in the testes is essential to make normal sperm. Where does it come from? Far from the testes, the brain's hypothalamus will release gonadotropin-releasing hormone, which stimulates the pituitary gland to release follicle-stimulating hormone and lutenizing hormone. These make their way via the blood stream to the testes. Lutenizing hormone stimulates other cells in the testes called *Leydig cells* to manufacture prodigious amounts of testosterone. Follicle-stimulating hormone now causes the Sertoli cells to produce androgen-binding proteins that will bind the testosterone produced in Leydig cells and concentrate it inside, where it will have its effect on the developing sperm. As the testosterone level increases, it also circulates throughout the body. When the correct concentration of testosterone (along with a concentration of the hormone inhibin, which is made in Sertoli cells) circulates back to the hypothalamus and pituitary gland of the brain, these structures are signaled to stop secreting their hormones. Without this stimulus, Leydig cells decrease production of testosterone until the circulating concentration drops to a level that will trigger the cycle to start all over again—keeping it in perfect balance.

Recall how the sperm are being kept from contact with the blood. They are locked behind very tight junctions between Sertoli cells that make a collective configuration called the *blood-testis barrier.* Why? A male does not begin producing sperm until puberty, and the markers on the new sperm cells have not been programmed into his immune system. The male's immune system is programmed to recognize specific combinations of protein markers on the outside of his cells as belonging to his own body—but that programming takes place while he is still in his mother's womb. Were it not for this barrier, sperm cells would be recognized as foreign cells by the male's own immune system and destroyed, rendering the male sterile. If the junction between Sertoli cells is broken, such as what happens when the testes become inflamed during an infection with the mumps virus, antibodies can make their way from the blood stream past the barrier and destroy the developing sperm.

Sperm placed inside a woman find themselves in a very hostile environment, with features that either destroy microscopic entities or block entrance into her body. The normal vaginal environment is very acidic (pH 3.5), which suppresses dangerous bacterial overgrowth but also kills sperm. Fluids produced by the male seminal vesicles are part of the semen and temporarily neutralize (pH 7.5) the acid. The neutral environment then activates the sperm. A thick, sticky mucus plug also blocks the small cervical opening into the uterus. However, another product of semen called *prostaglandins* causes this mucus to become more liquid-like. Not coincidentally, the mucus may also have been made even thinner by an estrogen surge in the woman around the time she ovulates an egg. Now sperm are able to swim through the mucus into the uterus—all the while converting substances in the mucus to energy.

The uterus is protected by millions of cells of the woman's immune system that kill microscopic invaders. This obstacle is overcome by substances in the semen that have local, but very broad-spectrum, immunosuppressive effects that blunt her immune response in the area of the semen. This may leave the woman vulnerable to infection, but another substance in semen, *seminalplasmin,* can kill bacteria and has a protective effect. Normally, coordinated movements of mobile hair-like projections called *cilia* on some cells lining the uterus, coupled with slight rhythmic contractions of the uterus, produce a defensive fluid current that pushes things out of the uterus—which would be impossible for the sperm to swim against. Yet another product of semen after making contact with the uterus causes these coordinated actions of the woman's uterus to reverse direction and pull the semen and sperm up into the uterus and assist the sperm on its journey.

Surprisingly, freshly deposited sperm are incapable of fertilizing an egg. Many features of the sperm are changed by substances that are made within the female reproductive tract. Remember the sperm's acrosomal body discussed earlier? One of the most important changes, known as *capacitation*, is when uterine secretions remove glycoproteins from the protective coat of the acrosome. This allows the erosive enzymes from many sperm (after contacting the egg) to break down a protective coat of cells around the egg and expose its cell membrane so that yet another sperm can make its way to the egg for fertilization. This elaborate coordination between female secretions and male sperm is protective for the male, since without the protective coat around the acrosome, high concentrations of sperm in a man's body could destroy the function of his reproductive organs if the erosive enzymes were released prematurely.

The acrosome is coated with the protein bindin that will adhere only to special species-specific receptors on the egg, ensuring that only sperm from the same species can fertilize the egg. In less than a second after the sperm's contact, many channels in the egg's membrane open, allowing an inrush of positively charged sodium ions. This creates an electrical charge across the outer surface of the egg that blocks other sperm from fertilizing it and inactivates all remaining bindin receptors on the egg. Concurrently, substances just inside the egg's cell membrane are released that bind up water molecules and cause the membrane to swell up to permanently detach any remaining sperm on the outside. These blocks prevent entrance of genetic material from any other sperm into the egg, which would be fatal to baby and may also be to mother. Once united, tube-like structures in the egg rapidly build and then project from the egg and pull the nucleus of the sperm into the egg—the first cell of a new person.

Amazing? Actually, the detail could go far beyond this simple description. As seen, the level of coordinated interaction to get any viable offspring exceeds the cellular level, extends past the reproductive system, pulls in the neurologic, hormonal, and circulatory systems, and demands substances that are produced independently by the male to modify the actions of the female body or the materials made by her—and vice versa. Evolutionary literature is rife with speculative stories about the origination of these processes but devoid of any real scientific evidence to explain them. The only viable explanation is that these processes were placed by the Lord Jesus in the first parents, Adam and Eve, fully functional right from the beginning.

Human Reproduction
Devotional Thought

The Pharisees also came to Him, testing Him, and saying to Him, "Is it lawful for a man to divorce his wife for just any reason?" And He answered and said to them, "Have you not read that He who made them at the beginning 'made them male and female,' and said, 'For this reason a man shall leave his father and mother and be joined to his wife, and the two shall become one flesh'? So then, they are no longer two but one flesh. Therefore what God has joined together, let not man separate." (Matthew 19:3-6)

The Lord Jesus Christ is quoting from both chapters 1 and 2 of Genesis, which is His affirmation that the creation account recorded in these chapters is both one-and-the-same event (not two different creation accounts) and is real history. These chapters, coupled with Genesis 4:1, clearly describe the creation of a man and a woman with fully functioning reproductive systems right from the beginning. This observation is scientifically accurate, as anything less than fully functioning systems would not result in children. The Lord Jesus is the Creator (John 1:1-5; Colossians 1:13-20; Hebrews 1:1-3) and, therefore, should know exactly what took place. How much better to believe His words than evolutionists' ever-changing stories that are intended to explain away a supernatural God and, in addition, make no sense scientifically.

Questions

1. What are two mechanisms that ensure that the DNA of a newly fertilized egg will be totally unlike any person that has ever lived before or ever will be born afterwards—resulting in an absolutely unique person?

2. Why are sperm different from other cells in a boy's body and may be subject to attack by a boy's own immune system? What is the name of the structure that protects the sperm, and what would be the result if it was not functioning right from the beginning?

3. It is interesting that products made in a man's body (coded by his DNA) vitally affect the functioning of the woman's body to allow fertilization, and products made in a woman's body are essential to the proper functioning of sperm. Name a few of these features. What would happen if they were not present? Why is this fact a major problem for evolution to explain?

Answers

1. Cellular mechanisms allow slight variations in the information contained on certain portions of the chromosomes to be shuffled during the divisions of sperm and egg so that there are variations from sperm to sperm and egg to egg. From a human perspective, it is random which sperm will fertilize an egg, as well as which egg will mature in an ovary every month and be ovulated. This results in a tremendous number of possible genetic combinations in the newly fertilized egg.

2. The boy's immune system is programmed to recognize specific combinations of protein markers on the outside of his cells as belonging to his own body—but that programming takes place while he is still in his mother's womb. The markers specific to sperm do not appear until a boy reaches puberty, on average at 12-14 years of age. So, the immune system has missed the opportunity to program itself as to the configuration of these markers. Sperm are protected by a structure (a series of tight junctions between Sertoli cells) in the testicle called the *blood-testis barrier*. Were it not for this barrier, sperm cells would be recognized as foreign cells by the boy's own immune system and be destroyed—rendering the boy sterile.

3. Fluids that are part of the semen temporarily blunt the female immune response in the uterus and neutralize the acidic environment of the vagina. Prostaglandins in semen cause a thick, sticky mucus plug blocking entrance of the cervix into the uterus to become more liquid-like and after making contact with the uterus cause the coordinated actions of the woman's uterus to reverse direction and pull the semen and sperm up into the uterus. Secretions in the uterus capacitate the sperm,

allowing erosive enzymes to be released at just the right time. Without these features, fertilization would be highly improbable, if not impossible. Getting a series of coordinated genetic mutations selected by nature to increase the function of one sex has never been observed and is exceedingly unlikely. Getting a series of genetic mistakes in one sex that is vital to the proper functioning of the other sex is essentially impossible.

Notes

_____

_____

_____

_____

_____

_____

_____

_____

_____

_____

_____

_____

_____

_____

_____

_____

_____

_____

_____

_____

_____

Notes

13
Human Gestation

The complexity of (handwritten)
interfacing (handwritten)

Admittedly, the prospect of pregnancy only applies to half of humanity, but the other half should find the process equally astounding. The real star of the show, however, is the developing baby, who was once viewed as a passive object being built by the mother's body. Nothing could be further from the truth. In terms of guiding implantation into the uterus all the way to breastfeeding, it is the baby/placenta unit that is the dynamic force in the orchestration of its own destiny.

The baby is a completely new individual, with unique genetic material that expresses foreign markers on his cells that are not recognized as "self" by the mother. The mother's immune system should destroy the new baby's first cells within just a few cell divisions, but substances secreted by the placenta and baby promote a complex suppression of the maternal immune response only within the implantation site of the uterus. The placental tissue that touches the uterus has decreased expression of markers that would provoke an immune response, and the mother's body therefore accepts it. Without this immunological acceptance, no baby would ever survive. And if the suppression of the mother's immune system were not localized, her health could be compromised. The maternal immune system helps control implantation of the embryo at just the right depth into the uterus. Without this exact balance of immune responses, the developing placenta could invade tissue all the way through the uterus and be fatal to the mother.

The mother's body is now under the control of a new person. A hormone produced by the baby's earliest cells travels in the mother's blood stream back to her ovary, causing a part of it to produce progesterone, the very important hormone that will calm uterine contractions and maintain the pregnancy. Later, the placenta will produce progesterone at even higher concentrations. Other hormones produced by the baby induce adaptations in the mother's body that are absolutely necessary for the baby's survival. These changes include a sizable expansion of the mother's blood volume, an increase in cardiac output, agents to modulate blood pressure, increases in blood flow to the kidneys, and cranking up the mother's metabolism. The placenta also extracts nutrients from maternal circulation so efficiently that the baby's needs are met first, then the mother's.

In the last weeks of pregnancy, estrogen produced by the baby reaches its highest levels in the mother's blood. This causes abundant receptors for the hormone oxytocin to form on the uterus' muscle cells and slowly opposes progesterone's quieting influence. At term, certain cells of the baby produce oxytocin, a powerful uterine muscle stimulant. Since the uterus is now highly sensitive to oxytocin, labor begins. As the baby descends, a pressure sensor in the birth canal sends a signal to the mother's brain and triggers her body to produce even more oxytocin—which causes stronger uterine contractions. The placenta produces the hormone relaxin, causing pelvic ligaments and the skin of the birth canal to relax, widen, and become more flexible. This increased motility allows a birth passage for the baby. And while in the womb, the baby made hormones that helped prepare the mother's breasts to produce milk. After delivery, newborn suckling induces episodic oxytocin secretion by the mother, which acts on breast ducts to cause milk let-down.

So it is the mother who is essentially passive, responding to signals emanating from the baby—even at times to her own detriment. Scientific research has shown that while the woman's reproductive organs and body are indispensable, they are not enough; it takes a baby to make a baby. The evidence is pretty compelling against speculations regarding a step-by-step evolutionary process leading to the complex systems that produce a baby. These systems were placed by the Lord Jesus in the first mother, Eve, fully functional right from the beginning.

Human Gestation
Devotional Thought

Now Mary arose in those days and went into the hill country with haste, to a city of Judah, and entered the house of Zacharias and greeted Elizabeth. And it happened, when Elizabeth heard the greeting of Mary, that the babe leaped in her womb; and Elizabeth was filled with the Holy Spirit. (Luke 1:39-41)

This wonderful passage provides insight into several profound truths as they relate to the development of a baby in his mother's womb. First, it is clear that the developing person in the womb is entirely distinct from—though dependent on—his mother, since he (the future John the Baptist) was already able to respond to the words of Mary very differently from his mother, Elizabeth. This child already had a unique body and his own personality, which are two representative elements of personhood. Second, John was already a very special person in the mind of the Lord, who had a specific plan for John's life. Though conception and gestation may seem like totally "natural" processes, it is the Lord who is sovereign over the start of every new life (Genesis 29:31; Deuteronomy 7:13). He enabled Elizabeth to conceive (Luke 1:7, 13), and He is keenly interested in children in the womb (see also Judges 13:5; Psalm 139:13-17; and Jeremiah 1:5).

Questions

1. A mother's immune system is well able to destroy a single cell of almost any living thing that invades her body. Why would her body naturally tend to destroy the newly fertilized egg since it is just an extension of her body? How is "acceptance" of pregnancy obtained?

2. Science has shown that while the mother's reproductive organs and body are indispensable, they are not enough—it takes a baby (and placenta) to make a baby. Why is the baby/placenta also indispensable? How can a slow, iterative evolutionary process over many generations explain the development of the interactions between baby and mother?

3. Does the fact that a chimpanzee, for example, has a similar reproductive system to a human prove that humans and chimpanzees had a common ancestor? Why are similarities between things in different creatures not good evidence for evolution?

Answers

1. The baby is not simply an extension of mother's body but is a completely new individual with unique genetic material, which expresses foreign markers on its cells that are not recognized as "self" by mother. Substances secreted by the placenta and baby promote suppression of the maternal immune response within the implantation site of the uterus. The mother's body therefore accepts it. The mother's immune system is locally suppressed but not eliminated, as her immune system helps to control implantation of the embryo. Without an exact balance of immune responses, the pregnancy could be fatal to the mother but would almost certainly result in destruction of the newly fertilized egg.

2. Interestingly, almost all of the building blocks to make hormones are extracted by the placenta from the mother's blood circulation, transferred to the placenta or organs inside the baby where the hormones are built, and then excreted back into the mother's circulation by the placenta. The placenta initially produces a vital hormone to maintain pregnancy called *progesterone*. The mother's metabolism and body are changed by other hormones produced by baby (and placenta) to induce a sizable expansion of blood volume, increase cardiac output, modulate blood pressure, increase the mother's metabolism, prepare the uterus to be stimulated by oxytocin, and even induce changes in breasts to prepare for feeding after delivery.

3. Similarities in anatomy are irrelevant in explaining the origin of the functions from the molecular level all the way to the

organism level. To observe that humans and chimpanzees have, for example, a similar uterus is not the issue. The issue is how the specialized cells with their specialized biochemical processes, organized in the specific layered pattern, vitally dependent on input from fully operating neurological, cardiovascular, and hormonal systems of any functional uterus first came about. Published evolutionary explanations are silent on this issue. They prefer to harp on similarities and explain origins with words like "arose" or "emerged," which are simple rationalizations and have no scientific meaning.

Notes

Notes

14
The complexity of the
Baby's First Breath

I n 1967 Dr. Christiaan Barnard performed the first heart transplant. Until that time, if someone's heart was taken out, they died. People were astounded to learn that not only was a man's heart removed, but a non-beating donor heart put in, restarted, and he lived. Years of design efforts and testing resulted in a sophisticated invention that circulated blood and functioned as patients' lungs to bring them oxygen—the all-important "heart-lung" machine.

No doubt in the same hospital in 1967 was a brand-new mother. Her baby had just made a similar transition of survival on an *exceedingly better* "lung machine," but no reporters covered it. Although the first event was a great feat of human engineering, the second has never been explained by any natural process.

Childbirth is so common it is easy to overlook the fact that a baby thrives in a total water world for nine months—a world that is *utterly impossible* for any person to live in immediately after their very first breath. That feat is accomplished by the baby possessing—only in the womb—blood vessels with a different arrangement and structure than an adult's.

The Adult Circulatory Arrangement

In an adult human heart, the bottom two chambers, the *ventricles*, do most of the higher-pressure pumping, pushing the blood through one-way valves away from the heart through arteries. The upper two, the *atria* (plural of "atrium"), receive blood under low pressure from veins and rapidly preload the ventricles by pushing blood into them, also through one-way valves.

The heart is also divided into left and right halves, separated by a solid wall of tissue called a *septum*. There are two circuits for blood flow from the heart: one to the lungs and back, and one to the body and back. The *right* heart starts blood on its circuit to the lungs, where less-oxygenated blood picks up a new load of oxygen. The *left* heart pumps freshly oxygenated blood at "normal" blood pressures (much higher than the right side) to the rest of the body.

In adults, oxygen-rich blood travels away from the heart through arteries under high pressures, and oxygen-poor blood flows toward the heart through veins under low pressure. Clearly, the heart and lungs are completely codependent in accomplishing the purpose of getting oxygen to all places in the body.

The Fetal Circulatory Arrangement

For a baby in the womb, almost everything about those vital functions is just the *opposite* for one important reason: the baby develops fully functional lungs that are yet inactive for oxygen exchange. Consequently, in order for a baby to survive, three major structural differences must exist that enable life in his temporary home.

First, the baby must have a substitute lung—a pretty tall order for even brilliant biomedical engineers. The placenta, a remarkable organ, has a brief existence, but it fulfills a myriad of vital functions—especially as the fetal lung *and* kidney. Second, the circuit to the lungs must be bypassed, so vessels must change to allow this temporary detour. (A new route that detours around a circuit is called a *shunt.*) Third, blood vessels must not only connect placenta to baby, but also inside from the point of attachment to normal vessels that lead to and from the heart. The umbilical cord meets the need for a placental-fetal connection, with one large-diameter vein and two smaller arteries. Inside the baby, these continue as the *umbilical vein* and *umbilical arteries.*

The umbilical vein carries oxygen-rich blood toward the heart. At a spot next to the liver, it connects to a large vein carrying less-oxygenated blood back to the heart. Interestingly, the two combined streams of blood do *not* tend to mix. It just happens that when they reach the right atrium, the more oxygenated blood stream is adjacent to a temporary opening in the septum, where it passes through to the left atrium because the blood pressure in the right side of baby's heart is higher than the left side—the opposite of the post-birth situation. The right heart still pumps blood to the lungs, but because the lungs have not yet expanded, the resistance to blood flow is very high and, therefore, the pressure is high. Some blood does make it to the right ventricle (about 10 percent) and flows through the lungs, which is the right amount to meet metabolic needs but *not* for oxygen-carrying purpose—which does not yet exist.

The temporary opening has a piece of septum tissue over it that is located in the left atrium. Thus, it acts like a "trap door" valve so that high pressure on the right side can push it open with each beat. In adults, it would make no sense for the artery carrying oxygen-poor blood to the lungs to connect by a big blood vessel to the artery carrying oxygen-rich blood (the aorta) to the body. But the baby does have this big connecting vessel in order to bypass the lungs and send oxygen-rich blood from the placenta to the body. Most of this blood travels to the part of the body with the highest oxygen demands—the growing brain.

So baby is content in the womb with temporary umbilical arteries and vein, a temporary opening in the septum, the temporary pulmonary artery-aorta shunt vessel, high pressure in the lungs and right side of the heart, and low pressure on the left side. With the onset of labor, culminating in delivery, that world is set to radically change. However, crucial mechanisms are built into the temporary structures that enable a safe transition out of the womb.

Vital Circulatory Changes Occurring at Birth

The umbilical cord vessels have features that respond to changes in quantities of oxygen dissolved in blood, stretching, substances commonly called *adrenaline*, and trauma. Obviously, during delivery and the severing of the cord all of these are present. The cord, which has an unusually strong muscle layer surrounding the vessels, reacts with a rapid and powerful constriction of the arteries and vein that is complete in less than a minute. This stops blood flow to and from the placenta, which has two effects. It greatly reduces the risk of either baby or mom losing a lot of blood and also causes an immediate drop in the amount of oxygen baby is getting.

Very sensitive sensors—inside certain blood vessels measuring carbon dioxide content, and also on the skin detecting temperature drops—stimulate the nervous system's breathing center. Under normal circumstances, increased carbon dioxide blood levels coupled with decreased body temperature after exiting the birth canal trigger an irresistible urge for baby to take a strong breath and inflate his lungs for the first time. The lungs have been prepared for this event by special cells producing a compound called *surfactant*, which significantly reduces the tension holding non-inflated lung tissues together—otherwise, forces required to open the lungs would be too high for almost all newborns to accomplish. Once inflated, pressures necessary to pump blood through the lungs *drop 90 percent* from their intra-womb high values.

Thus, pressure in the right side of the heart immediately drops well below the pressure in the left side. The "trap door" valve (actually two flaps of skin that neatly fold and interlock when pushed together) covering the septum's temporary opening in the left atrium is pressured shut. Cells begin to grow over the edges of the valve, fusing it to the septum. Less than a minute after birth, signals from baby's nervous system cause strong sphincter muscles to close off the umbilical vein where it attaches near the liver and also close off the temporary pulmonary artery-aorta shunt. (That large vessel permanently closes over the next one to two days.)

The baby's body has started all changes that continue through adulthood. During the next year, those internal umbilical vein and arteries transform from blood vessels into stabilizing ligaments. So in the one critical minute after delivery, the baby's body has initiated actual structural changes enabling it to survive in its radically different environment with all temporary vessels, shunts, and openings functionally closed in the first 30 minutes.

Conclusion

The reality of fetal to newborn circulatory changes is this: structures *indispensable* for life in the womb are *incompatible* with life out of it, and at birth all structures are rapidly reversed, resulting in the *opposite* effect on survival. In either case, if the offspring dies, evolution ends. Darwin wrote, "If it could be demonstrated that any complex organ existed which could not possibly have been formed by numerous, successive, slight modifications, my theory would absolutely break down."[1]

Consider it broken...if not a catastrophic failure. Why? Given that a transplanted heart living inside someone is truly an incredible achievement—at what level of accomplishment is getting a *whole person* to live *inside* another person? Absolutely incredible—which is what the Lord Jesus Christ is! As clearly seen, He creates, He directs, He provides, He cares—indeed, everything He does is beautiful beyond description.

Reference
1. Darwin, C. 1859. *On the Origin of Species.* London: John Murray, 189.

Baby's First Breath
Devotional Thought

*Jesus answered and said to him, "Most assuredly,
I say to you, unless one is born again, he cannot
see the kingdom of God." Nicodemus said to Him,
"How can a man be born when he is old? Can he
enter a second time into his mother's womb and
be born?" Jesus answered, "Most assuredly, I say
to you, unless one is born of water and the Spirit,
he cannot enter the kingdom of God. That which
is born of the flesh is flesh, and that which is born
of the Spirit is spirit. Do not marvel that I said to
you, 'You must be born again.'" (John 3:3-7)*

The number of changes that take place within the baby's body
within minutes of being born are extraordinary and permanent.
The changes that happen to a person when they are born again
are far more impressive. Why? Being born again means that a
person was actually "dead" in sin (Ephesians 2:1) but is now made
"alive" in Christ (Romans 6:11) and can "walk in newness of life"
(Romans 6:4). Affections and desires are all changed. Spiritual
truth actually means something important to them and is no
longer considered foolishness (1 Corinthians 2:14). They can
actually have "the mind of Christ" (1 Corinthians 2:16). The gift
of a new, noble purpose for living, bearing eternally good results,
replaces a self-centered drive that sought after only temporary
accomplishments (Philippians 3:12-14; Colossians 3:1). Indeed,
"if anyone is in Christ, he is a new creation; old things have passed
away; behold, all things have become new" (2 Corinthians 5:17).

Questions

1. Darwin wrote, "If it could be demonstrated that any complex organ existed which could not possibly have been formed by numerous, successive, slight modifications, my theory would absolutely break down" (*On the Origin of Species*, 189). Why does the fetal circulatory system pose a challenge to evolutionary explanations?

2. In some fetal babies, the opening between the septum in the atria (foramen ovale of the heart) does not close completely or the shunt between the pulmonary artery and aorta (ductus arteriosis) remains patent. These conditions may require surgical intervention. Evolutionists claim that these imperfections demonstrate a long evolutionary development of trial and error. Is this assertion valid?

3. Human beings engage in activities that are analogous to a baby living in the womb. What are some of those activities? What are some challenges engineers face with these activities?

Answers

1. No baby could survive the water world or the abrupt change to the air world with circulatory features requiring numerous, successive, slight modifications—since *no baby* means *no natural selection* of any traits, which means *no evolution*. The fetal circulatory system is a reality that forces Darwin's theory to "absolutely break down."

2. What this assertion really shows is how poor evolutionary theory is and what flimsy evidence evolutionists are willing to accept as support. This is yet another example of the circular reasoning that is rampant in evolutionary theory, i.e., "evolution predicts that systems may not work perfectly well in some instances; those instances where they do not work perfectly well are evidence of evolution." This prediction only makes sense in the context that evolution is already assumed to be true. In addition, it lacks scientific rigor because it is overly broad and almost any observation can be made to fit it. Evolutionists completely overlook the fact that the entire system shows all the features of design as well as incredible genetic coordination between baby, placenta, and mother— critical areas really lacking any evolutionary explanation.

3. Activity that totally removes a person from their air environment, like going underwater in a submarine or traveling to the moon in space, is similar to life in the womb. Engineers had to devise ways to get people oxygen to breathe (usually carried in tanks or made from water); remove carbon dioxide; provide food (usually carried along); safely dispose of urine and feces; and provide protection from the new external

environment (by living inside a ship of some type). All of these were major engineering hurdles that are still being improved. However, not even the most up-to-date, high-tech methods come close to the systems that support a baby in the womb.

Notes

_____

_____

_____

_____

_____

_____

_____

_____

_____

_____

_____

_____

_____

_____

_____

_____

_____

_____

_____

_____

_____

_____

Notes

_____

_____

_____

_____

_____

_____

_____

_____

_____

_____

_____

_____

_____

_____

_____

_____

_____

_____

_____

_____

_____

About the Author

Dr. Randy Guliuzza is a captivating speaker who presents well-documented and often humorous scientific and biblical talks to audiences of all ages. He has represented ICR in several scientific debates at secular universities and in other forums. Dr. Guliuzza has a B.S. in Engineering from the South Dakota School of Mines and Technology, a B.A. in theology from Moody Bible Institute, an M.D. from the University of Minnesota, and a Master of Public Health from Harvard University. Dr. Guliuzza served nine years in the Navy Civil Engineer Corps and is a registered Professional Engineer. In 2008, he retired as Lt. Col. from the U.S. Air Force, where he served as 28th Bomb Wing Flight Surgeon and Chief of Aerospace Medicine. He is the author of *Clearly Seen: Constructing Solid Arguments for Design*, and a contributor to *Guide to Creation Basics, Creation Basics & Beyond, Guide to the Human Body,* and the *Made in His Image* DVD series.

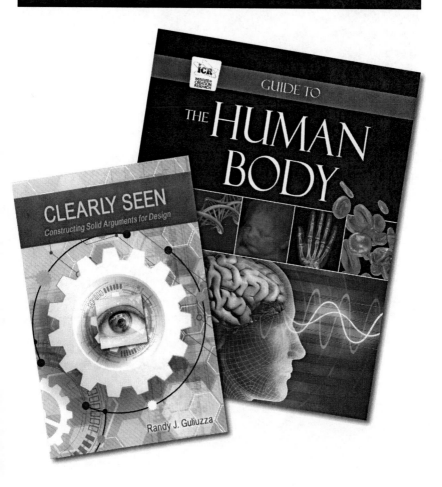

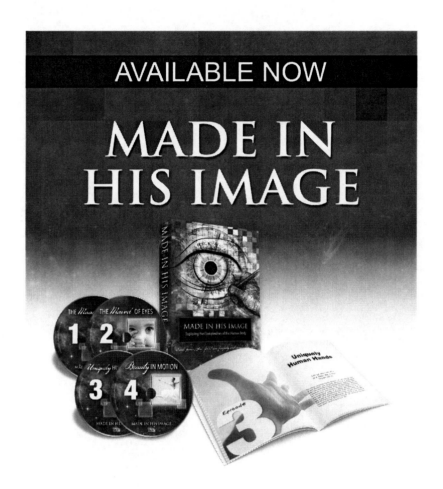

CPSIA information can be obtained
at www.ICGtesting.com
Printed in the USA
FFOW03n2009260317
33746FF